I WON'T!

BY

GINA WILKINS

D0714311

CAMBRIDGESHIRE LIBRARIES
MAR 1996
MB

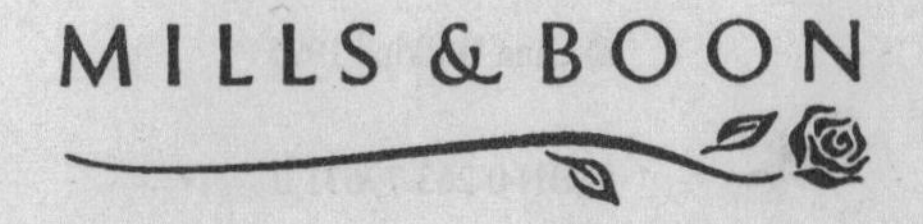

For Linda Varner Palmer,
who reminds me often
that we truly love this job

DID YOU PURCHASE THIS BOOK WITHOUT A COVER?
If you did, you should be aware it is **stolen property** as it was reported *unsold and destroyed* by a retailer. Neither the author nor the publisher has received any payment for this book.

All the characters in this book have no existence outside the imagination of the author, and have no relation whatsoever to anyone bearing the same name or names. They are not even distantly inspired by any individual known or unknown to the author, and all the incidents are pure invention.

All rights reserved including the right of reproduction in whole or in part in any form. This edition is published by arrangement with Harlequin Enterprises II B.V. The text of this publication or any part thereof may not be reproduced or transmitted in any form or by any means, electronic or mechanical, including photocopying, recording, storage in an information retrieval system, or otherwise, without the written permission of the publisher.

This book is sold subject to the condition that it shall not, by way of trade or otherwise, be lent, resold, hired out or otherwise circulated without the prior consent of the publisher in any form of binding or cover other than that in which it is published and without a similar condition including this condition being imposed on the subsequent purchaser.

MILLS & BOON and the Rose Device are trademarks of the publisher. TEMPTATION is a trademark of Harlequin Enterprises II B.V., used under licence.
First published in Great Britain 1996
by Harlequin Mills & Boon Limited, Eton House, 18-24 Paradise Road, Richmond, Surrey TW9 1SR

© Gina Wilkins 1995

ISBN 0 263 79631 0

21 - 9603

Printed in Great Britain by
BPC Paperbacks Ltd

Prologue

CASE BRANNIGAN was getting married. There were a lot of people who would never have believed it. He was finding it rather hard to believe, himself.

The tropical scents and exotic sounds of Cancún, Mexico, drifted through the open windows on one side of the snug little vacation cottage, adding to the fantasy feel of the day. Case began to whistle as he worked on the knot of his tie. Damn, but he felt good.

The sounds of soft laughter and muted conversation grew slightly louder, then faded, telling him that at least two people—probably one of the many couples currently in residence at the resort—had passed close by his cabin. He had an uncharacteristically whimsical urge to run to the window and invite them to his wedding, which was to take place in a little over half an hour.

Though this was intended as a private wedding, with only the bridal couple, an officiant and a hired witness in attendance, Case suddenly found himself wishing for a more traditional ceremony. Candles and lace, flowers, family and friends. Tiny flower girls, ushers in penguin suits, guests in wedding finery, a tipsy uncle making bawdy toasts.

Tradition. Something Case had never had with his unusual upbringing. Something he'd always fiercely craved.

And now, with his thirty-fifth birthday looming close, he meant to make up for the lack. He was going to have a normal life. Wife, kids, a house and a yard. A dog. Maybe two. Sunday dinners, Little League, school plays, camping trips with the kids.

It would be a nice change to sleep in the woods without wondering who might be out there tracking him down.

Tie in place, he took a moment to check his appearance in the mirror. His habitually shaggy dark hair was neatly combed—unusual enough, in itself. His slightly squared jaw was clean-shaven, exposing the shallow cleft in his chin. His dark suit was freshly pressed, lint-free, his white shirt pristine. There were people who would have had a tough time recognizing him, he thought with a chuckle. People he hoped he never saw again.

Satisfied with his appearance, he turned toward the bed, where he'd laid the marriage license and the tiny box that held a small, plain gold band. He slipped both into the inside pocket of his jacket. He would buy a diamond to accompany the band as soon as he had a chance, he promised himself. Or would Maddie prefer an emerald, or maybe a ruby?

Having met her less than two weeks ago, there were still quite a few things he had yet to learn about her.

Two weeks. He laughed softly and shook his head. Who would have believed it?

He'd come to Cancún to rest and regroup, to make some heavy decisions about what he wanted to do for the rest of his life. Weary and burned-out after years of government service, he had found himself craving something he couldn't define, aching with a need that he hadn't been able to understand. And then he'd met Maddie. Sweet Maddie Carmichael. And suddenly everything had become clear.

He now knew that what he'd needed had been a woman. A partner. A friend. Soft arms. Gentle smiles. A warm heart. All that sappy stuff he'd scorned so loudly in his reckless youth.

He'd known within hours that Maddie would be the perfect wife in the "Normal Life" he envisioned for himself. A small-town girl with deep roots to her community and her family. Pretty, in a wholesome, girl-next-door way. Sweet-natured, a bit naive, perhaps. She'd admitted that she enjoyed cooking—she even owned a family-style restaurant along with her father back home in Mississippi. She loved children. Her hobbies were needlework and watercolor painting.

He couldn't have found a more perfect bride if he'd created her himself.

Case had approached his courtship of Maddie with the same intensity and single-minded determination that had made him so dangerous—and successful, in his career. He'd swept her off her feet, flattered her, wooed her, enticed her. Dazzled her with romance. Deliberately kept her so dazed and bemused that she—who admitted she was rarely impulsive—had agreed to marry a man who was little more than a stranger to her. He had promised her the moon—and he had every intention of trying to obtain it for her. It was the least she deserved for rescuing him from a life of bleak, bitter loneliness.

He doubted that anyone had ever pursued her with bolder tenacity. He knew he'd never invested this much effort into any other woman. To be painfully honest, he'd always considered himself rather awkward and uncomfortable around women, choosing to spend occasional time only with the ones who hadn't made it necessary for him to pursue them.

But then, no other woman had ever mattered this much to him.

He patted his pocket, reassuring himself that the license and ring were in place. He looked into the mirror once more, noting that he still looked presentable. And then he glanced at his watch.

Half an hour to go. Half an hour of being single. Half an hour alone.

A quiver went through his flat stomach. Maybe a touch of nerves. Certainly a healthy shot of anticipation—after all, he hadn't even made love to his pretty bride yet. He'd been determined to do this thing right—a traditional, if rather hasty, courtship, a traditional, and not-at-all hurried, wedding night. His pulse rate increased at the thought of that long night ahead.

A series of quick, sharp raps on the motel-room door made him look around in question. Who in the world...? Maddie was supposed to meet him at the judge's office. He wasn't expecting anyone else.

He crossed the room and opened the door. And then muttered a curse and tried to shut it again.

A slender, coral-tipped hand shoved from the other side. "I've got to talk to you," the tall, stunning redhead in the hallway insisted in a husky voice Case knew all too well.

"Go away, Jade. I'm busy."

"Come on, let me in. This is important."

"I'm getting married in half an hour, damn it."

Jade's emerald eyes were filled with sympathy. He'd never seen her look at him quite that way before. He didn't like seeing the emotion there now. "I'm afraid you're going to have to postpone that," she said quietly.

Case shook his head, though a sick feeling of foreboding was spreading through him. "No way."

Jade reached inside the jacket of her beautifully tailored dark green suit. "I have something here I think will convince you," she said in a carefully uninflected voice that made Case go very still.

Oh, damn, Maddie. I'm so sorry.

FOR AT LEAST the tenth time in less than twenty minutes, Maddie checked the time on her watch, aware that she was being surreptitiously—and sympathetically—watched from across the small office by the justice of the peace and his wife. Case was late, over twenty minutes late. The ceremony should have been over by now. They should already be married.

So where was he?

"Would you like to call the resort again, Miss Carmichael?" the middle-aged officiant asked in slightly accented English.

Maddie managed a smile and shook her head. She'd already called Case's rooms twice. There'd been no answer either time. "I'm sure he's on his way," she said with a confidence that was rapidly fading. "He's obviously been detained. By traffic, perhaps."

Señor and Señora Ruiz nodded agreeably, though Maddie could see the doubt mirrored in their dark eyes. They thought she'd been stood up, she realized.

Oh, God—what if they were right?

She twisted her fingers in front of her, her fair-complexioned cheeks warming with an embarrassed flush. What was she doing here? she asked herself in a sudden surge of panic. How had she allowed herself to get into this painfully awkward situation? She'd only come to Cancún on a vacation—a vacation she'd won through a supermarket sweepstakes, for crying out loud!

She'd left Mississippi in the hope of getting some rest, maybe finding a bit of excitement to inject in her otherwise routine life. She hadn't expected to find herself involved in a vacation romance—and she certainly hadn't planned on marrying a man she'd met by accident on a sandy beach! Less than two weeks ago, for heaven's sake. But she was here now, fully prepared to carry through with the impulsive promise she'd given.

Where the hell was Case?

She smoothed her damp palms down the side of her floating white eyelet sundress—the only garment she'd brought along that had looked in the least bridal. And then she brushed a strand of mousy brown hair away from the sidepiece of her glasses. Case would be here, she reassured herself, remembering the intense look in his unusual gray eyes as he'd begged her to marry him. He couldn't have looked at her that way if he hadn't meant it—could he?

A tentative knock on the door made Maddie catch her breath and whirl toward the sound. *Case?*

The shy-looking young woman who entered the office was someone Maddie recognized. "Carmelita?" she asked in surprise. "What are you doing here?"

Carmelita was an employee at the resort where Maddie and Case had been staying. Maddie had found herself drawn to the woman's sweet smile and open manner, and had begun to consider Carmelita a friend—one she'd needed badly as she'd tumbled into love with a stranger. Needing to talk to another woman, she'd confided her confusion and bedazzlement to Carmelita, who was young enough and romantic enough to be fascinated by the whirlwind courtship taking place in front of her. She had even given Maddie a lace-trimmed handkerchief to carry during the wedding ceremony—for luck, she'd said shyly.

Carmelita wasn't smiling now. Her huge black eyes were liquid with sympathy. "I have a note for you," she said simply, holding out her hand.

Maddie stared at the folded square of white paper with a sick feeling deep inside her. Somehow, she already knew what it said. "He isn't coming, is he?" she whispered.

Carmelita shook her head. "He had to leave. Read the note."

Something in the way Carmelita was looking at her made Maddie tense. "When did he leave?"

"Not long ago. They—he seemed to be in a great hurry," the young woman answered carefully, quickly rephrasing the sentence.

But Maddie had caught the stammered word. "They?" she repeated. "He didn't leave alone?"

Torn by loyalty and compassion, Carmelita shook her head. "No. There was a woman."

"A woman?" Maddie pressed a hand to her aching stomach.

"*Sí*. She was tall, very pretty and she had red hair. Perhaps it was his sister," Carmelita suggested helpfully, unaware that Case had told Maddie several times that he had no family, no one at all. "Perhaps there was an emergency at his home, yes? Read the note, Maddie," she repeated, holding it out insistently.

Maddie's hand was shaking when she finally made herself take the note. She opened it carefully, as though afraid it would explode in her face.

> Maddie, I'm sorry. Something urgent has come up, and I have to leave. The wedding must be postponed. Go home, and wait for me. I'll call you as soon as I can.
>
> Case

Something died inside Maddie. And something else was born in its place, conceived in pain and grief and blazing hot temper.

Sweet Maddie Carmichael would never be quite the same.

1

THE BARELY COHERENT directions Case had gotten from the gawky boy at the service station had proven more reliable than he'd expected. As instructed, he turned left at the third and final traffic light in the small town of Mitchell's Fork, Mississippi, and discovered that he'd reached his destination. He pulled into the surprisingly crowded parking lot, turned off his ignition and released a deep sigh.

It had taken him too damned long to get here.

A large sign identified the restaurant—Mike and Maddie's. Seeing Maddie's name made Case reach up to tug at his tie, feeling as though it had suddenly tightened on him.

Funny how clearly he could still picture her after all these months. As though he'd seen her only a few minutes ago. Her sweet, oval face, framed in long, light brown hair. Mousy brown, she'd called it with a wrinkle of her little nose, but Case had liked the soft gleam and delicate scent of the below-shoulder-length mass. Her mouth was soft and full, usually unpainted since she admitted to a chronic tendency to chew off her lipstick. He hadn't minded; he'd never cared for the heavily made-up look. Maddie's natural prettiness had appealed to him from the first time he saw her.

Her eyes were her best feature. They were a clear, purply blue, only partially obscured by the glasses that compensated for their myopia. Case could still remember catching his breath when he'd removed those glasses to kiss her for the first time, and had been exposed to his first unobstructed look at those lovely eyes. He'd been struck by an uncharacteristically possessive satisfaction that few people received the full impact of Maddie's eyes.

She was small—almost a foot shorter than his six feet three inches—and gently rounded rather than model thin. He had been vaguely annoyed when she'd reluctantly skipped the delicious desserts and had wistfully passed over the rich, high-calorie dishes on the resort menu. She'd considered herself waging a constant battle against ten extra pounds. Case had thought she looked just fine. In fact, he'd been decidedly impatient to get much more intimately acquainted with her soft curves.

He'd had plenty of time to regret his atypical nobility in not taking her to bed the first chance he'd had to do so.

His sleek, powerful Ferrari looked oddly out of place among the pickup trucks, four-wheel-drive vehicles and family sedans crowding the parking lot. He frowned thoughtfully at the observation, wondering if he should trade it for a Jeep or a Bronco. After all, he wanted to fit in here.

He reached for the door handle and winced as he swung his left leg out of the car. He had to brace himself as he climbed out. He couldn't quite trust that leg not to buckle on him. It had only been two weeks since he'd tossed the hated crutches aside. The doctors had told him he was damned lucky he could walk at all.

Funny how nervous he was. He could burst into a roomful of armed drug dealers with more confidence than he was feeling now.

He cleared his throat, ran a hand through his freshly trimmed hair and made a quick check of his appearance. His dark suit—the one he'd intended to be married in—hung loosely on him. He'd regained only five of the fifteen pounds he'd lost during the past six months. He knew his face was more gaunt than it had been, and his eyes were heavily shadowed. He walked with a limp now, and several ugly new scars had been added to the older ones scattered across his battered thirty-five-year-old body.

He hoped Maddie wouldn't be too dismayed by the changes in him, though it was more likely that her gentle heart would swell with sympathy. At the moment, he wouldn't mind a little TLC—and he wasn't above using her tender pity to get him back into her good graces.

He'd come too far to give up the dream now.

He straightened and limped toward the entrance of the restaurant, his shoulders squared with renewed determination. Case Brannigan was a man on a mission. And, recent history notwithstanding, he rarely failed when he set his sights on a goal.

THE RESTAURANT specialized in home-style cooking. In keeping with its simple menu, the establishment's decor was classic country. A long front porch held a row of oversize wooden rockers, discreetly marked for sale, and the huge double doors were made of weathered barnwood. The lobby had been designed to resemble a country store, with rows of old-fashioned merchandise for sale—cookbooks, hard candies, simple toys, country-chic home decorations, even jars of honey and jams.

The place was crowded on this Sunday afternoon, most of the diners dressed in what appeared to be Sunday-best clothing, making Case suspect that this was a popular after-church stop. There were quite a few people browsing through the merchandise as they waited for a table or made their way out after eating.

Case searched the milling crowd for Maddie's familiar face. He didn't see her, but told himself to be patient. His rarely fallible instincts told him she was here.

A painfully thin, awkwardly tall woman in a blue denim dress with a red-checked apron looked up from the reception stand in the doorway to the main dining room. "You eatin' alone?" she asked him in the broad, rural Mississippi drawl he'd become accustomed to since arriving in the state that morning.

"Yes," he replied, though he hoped he wouldn't be alone for long. "Can you tell me where I might find—"

His question was interrupted by a quick, shrill whistle. "Table four's ready, Hazel," a young man called from somewhere behind the woman.

Hazel waved an acknowledgment, glanced at the scribbled pad in front of her and called out in one breath, "Anderson-party-of-five-your-table's-ready." And then she looked at Case. "Name?" she asked.

A bit disconcerted by the bustling informality of the place, Case started to answer. "It's Branni—"

Again he was interrupted, this time by a very large man in beltless polyester slacks and a food-spotted white shirt. "Pork chops were pert' near overcooked today, Hazel," he complained as he pushed past the family of five on their way to table four. "You tell Mike he better watch that or he's going to lose my business."

"Leon, you been threatening to quit eating here for the past five years," Hazel retorted, obviously unconcerned. "You know darned well you ain't going to find any better food in this part of the state. Now quit your gripin' and get along with you."

The heavy man tugged a battered cap over his thin brown hair. "See you next week," he growled on his way out. "And I sure hope the food's better then."

Hazel shook her overteased gray head and muttered beneath her breath, "He liked the food any better, he'd explode for sure." She glanced back at Case, as though surprised to see him still standing there. "What did you say your name was?"

"Brannigan," he replied. "I'm looking for—"

A blonde with a stack of plastic-coated menus precariously balanced in her arms dashed out of the dining room. With her back turned to Case, she dumped the menus in the wooden rack attached to one side of the reception stand. Case sighed and moved out of the way, noting only briefly that the blonde was young and slender and that the blue-denim and red-checked uniform fit her much more flatteringly than it did Hazel.

"How many are waiting?" she asked Hazel when the menus had been secured in the rack.

Case stiffened in response to the woman's voice. He frowned and looked at her more closely. It couldn't be—

"Two parties of two, and one family of six. Oh, and this man," Hazel said, looking apologetically back at Case. "Sorry, what was the name?"

The blonde glanced around—and froze. She and Case spoke at the same time.

"Brannigan."

"Brannigan!"

Aware that she'd said his name with something uncomfortably akin to loathing, Case stared in near shock at the woman facing him. "Maddie?"

What the hell had she done to her hair? The formerly long, brown tresses had been sheared to collar-length and streaked with glittering gold highlights. She wore it loose and fluffed and a bit tousled, as though it had been combed with her fingers—or someone else's. Her glasses were gone, exposing her large, purply blue eyes, which were emphasized by long, skillfully darkened lashes. Her soft mouth had been painted a deep rose—and she hadn't chewed the color away.

The short-sleeved denim dress was cut in a low scoop that bared a tantalizing expanse of her soft chest, the skirt was short enough to reveal entirely too much of her shapely legs. He'd only ever seen her in prim, almost excessively modest clothing. Like Case, she'd lost weight—but he had no reason to believe her loss was due to poor health. As a matter of fact, she looked fit and trim and tanned—she looked stunning.

And Case wasn't at all sure he approved.

"Maddie?" he said again, when she only continued to stare back at him.

Her face, which had paled at the sight of him, suddenly went red. Case smiled slightly in response to her blush. Of course, she was surprised to see him. He certainly didn't blame her.

And then he realized that the heightened color he'd arrogantly attributed to embarrassed pleasure had been a sign of a kindling temper. Her eyes sparked, her chin lifted, her slender body straightened, her hands clenched into fists at her side. "Get out," she said.

He felt his jaw go slack. He hadn't actually expected her to throw herself in his arms—well, okay, maybe he had—but surely he hadn't heard her correctly. Surely she hadn't just ordered him out of her restaurant.

He held out a hand to her. "Maddie, it's me," he said inanely, though she'd already said his name. "Case."

"Go away," she said, more loudly this time, causing several bystanders to look around in surprised curiosity. "Get out!"

"What the—" He couldn't believe this. This couldn't be the woman he'd met at that resort in Cancún six months ago. The sweet, shyly eager young woman who'd responded so touchingly to his ardent courtship, who'd allowed him to sweep her into his arms and into a day-long engagement to be married.

Was it possible that Maddie had a less friendly twin? "Maddie?" he asked again, uncertainly.

"Maddie?" A busy-looking man with pale blue eyes and thinning hair the same light brown Maddie's had once been came through the dining room doorway. "What's going on out here?"

Hazel cleared her throat. "This man wants a table," she explained. "Maddie—uh—asked him to leave."

"We're full," Maddie said, her gaze holding Case's in a glittering glare. "No more tables. He'll have to find someplace else to eat. Someplace in another state, preferably."

Hazel choked.

The man Case assumed to be Maddie's father looked shocked. "Madelyn!" he said. "Is that any way to talk to a customer? Whatever has gotten into you?"

"That's what a lot of people have been wanting to know lately," Hazel muttered.

Case ignored all of them except Maddie. "We have to talk," he told her.

She tossed her head, causing the gold-streaked waves to ripple softly around her face. "I'm busy."

"Damn it, Maddie—"

She turned on one high heel and stalked away.

Case moved to follow her.

Maddie's father, the scowling Hazel and a beefy, bearded man in a red-plaid flannel shirt moved together in the doorway, blocking Case's path.

"Didn't sound to me like she wants to talk to you," the flannel-draped mountain growled from behind his bushy black beard.

Case didn't know where the guy had come from, but he eyed the massively muscled arms warily before turning to the smaller, less intimidating man who was wearing a worried frown. "You're Maddie's father?"

The man nodded. "I'm Mike Carmichael. Uh—who are you?"

"Case Brannigan. I'm sure she told you about me. I need to talk to her."

"Case Brannigan?" Carmichael repeated in confusion. And then he shook his head. "She's never mentioned you." He glanced at Hazel, as though for confirmation.

Hazel shrugged one bony shoulder. "Never heard of him."

"Me, neither," the bearded hulk muttered. "Want me to throw him out, Mike?" He sounded almost gleefully eager.

Case instinctively backed up a step.

Mike took note of Case's visible limp, then shook his head. "Maybe I'd better have a little talk with him first, Andy. You go on back to your dinner, okay?"

Case was still trying to deal with the staggering news that Maddie had never even mentioned him to her father. She'd led Case to believe that she and her widowed father were very close. Why hadn't she told the man that she was engaged to be married?

The answer, of course, was all too obvious after the way Maddie had received him. She no longer considered herself engaged. Case fully intended to set her straight. Just as soon as he managed to speak to her.

Mike Carmichael was still watching him warily. Case held his chin high, tried his best to look like a respectable son-in-law prospect and plastered on a respectful smile as he offered his hand. "It's very nice to meet you, Mr. Carmichael. I'm Case Brannigan. Maddie's fiancé."

FORTUNATELY, Mike Carmichael was too busy with the Sunday lunch crowd to talk to Case, particularly when it became apparent that Maddie had left. "I'll want to talk to you," Mike warned, even as he was being called from three directions.

"Just tell me how to find Maddie," Case responded. "She and I will both talk to you later."

"Didn't look to me like Maddie wanted to be found," Mike mused out loud, studying him so intently that Case was tempted to squirm like an embarrassed teenager meeting his prom date's parent.

"It's not as bad as it looked," he assured Maddie's father. "She's just annoyed with me right now. She'll understand after I've had a chance to explain everything to her."

"Mike! We really need you in the kitchen," someone yelled.

Mike sighed and ran a hand through his thinning hair. "I have to go. Maddie's probably back at the house by now. Hazel, here, will give you directions. And you watch your step with my daughter, you hear?"

"I will," Case promised, impatient to leave.

Mike hesitated a moment longer, but then turned away in response to another frantic call.

Case released a silent breath and looked at the frowning Hazel. "Directions?" he prompted, knowing she had listened to every word.

Her frown deepened. She looked Case over from the top of his dark head to his dusty leather shoes. "When did you and Maddie meet?" she demanded.

Case had never been a patient man, and had never bothered expressing himself politely when his tolerance was tested. It took all his willpower not to snap at this woman to just give him the directions without the chitchat. Something told him he'd never get anything out of her if he hacked her off. "We met in Cancún," he admitted.

"Ah-hah!" she barked. "Thought so. Maddie ain't been the same since she came back from that vacation. Dyed her hair, got those contact lenses, hasn't eaten enough to keep a bird alive. Goin' out with Jackson Babbit, when everyone knows what kind of man *he* is, and then telling everyone she's going off to Europe before long and don't know when she'll be back."

Case scowled. Who the hell was Jackson Babbit? And just what kind of man *was* he?

And what was this about Maddie planning to leave for Europe? He spoke quickly, before the grumbled monologue could resume. "How do I get to her house from here?"

Ignoring the controlled chaos around them, Hazel shook her head, still following her own line of thought. "I told her when she won that trip to Mexico that she should wait until someone could go with her. It wasn't like her to take off on her own like that. But she was hell-bent to go, and sure enough, she came back a different person. She was always so sweet and quiet and good-natured before. Did everything anyone asked of her, seemed content with the way things had always been around here."

She shook a finger at Case, as though deciding he was to blame. "Since that trip, she's acted like one of those women's libbers. Speaks her mind whether anyone asks or not. Dropped out of the Mitchell's Fork Ladies'

Charity Club—her mama would turn over in her grave for that. There's been a Carmichael in the L.C.C. since the club was founded."

"Maybe you could just—"

"And now she's decided she's got to go off and 'find herself.' Don't know why she thinks she can do that in Europe. 'You can find yourself right here in Mitchell's Fork,' I told her. 'Where you think you been hiding for the past twenty-nine years, hmm?'"

"I really wish you'd—"

"Know what she said to me?" Hazel answered before Case had a chance to respond. "'The old Maddie Carmichael has been hiding in Mitchell's Fork for the past twenty-nine years,' she said. 'There's a new one out there somewhere, and I plan to find her.' Ain't that the damnedest fool thing you ever heard?"

Everything Hazel had rambled on about made Case increasingly anxious to get to Maddie. "Look," he said, moving toward the reception stand and giving her the glare that had made very large and very mean men take a step backward. "Are you going to give me directions to Maddie's house or am I going to have to find it on my own?"

To his utter surprise, Hazel gave a crack of laughter, looking far from intimidated. "I like a man with some pepper to 'im," she said. "You remind me of my late husband, Roy. He was always one to—"

"Just give me the damned directions!" Case roared, finally losing all semblance of patience.

"Want me to throw him out of here, Hazel?" the massive man in the flannel shirt yelled from his table twenty feet behind Hazel's stand, causing nearly everyone else in the place to look around expectantly.

"No, you finish your lunch, Andy," Hazel called back. "I was just giving the man directions."

And then she proceeded to do so, to Case's great relief.

MADDIE WAS still furiously pacing the length of her bedroom when the telephone on her nightstand rang—her private line. She glared at the instrument as though trying to see who waited at the other end of the wire. On the third ring, she snatched the receiver. "Hello?" she said, hoping it wasn't Case Brannigan.

"Maddie? It's Jill. You remember—your best friend?"

Frowning at the odd tone in her friend's voice, Maddie asked, "What's going on, Jill?"

"Good question. Why don't you tell me?"

"Tell you what?"

"Why don't you tell me how on earth you could have gotten yourself engaged without ever even mentioning it to me. Honestly, Maddie, we've always—"

"Engaged?" Maddie repeated, startled. "What on earth are you talking about?"

"The same thing everyone else in town is talking about. Some gorgeous male walked into the restaurant and introduced himself to your father as your fiancé—right in front of half the population of Mitchell's Fork. So what have you been holding back, hmm? Does he have anything to do with the trip to Europe you've been planning? And does Jackson know about this guy?"

Maddie winced. *Jackson. Oh, heavens!* And what the hell was Case Brannigan doing, breezing into town and introducing himself as her fiancé? If he seriously thought their so-called engagement was still on, then Maddie intended to set him straight in no uncertain terms!

"This is all a big mistake, Jill," she said stiffly. "Trust me, I'm not engaged. To anyone."

"That's not what your fiancé is saying," Jill retorted, though she sounded more amused than hurt now.

"I don't *have* a fiancé!"

"Okay, okay. You don't have to shout."

Maddie grimaced and lowered her voice. "Sorry. I'm just . . . a bit stressed at the moment."

Jill laughed. "I can certainly understand why. So who is this guy, Maddie? Where did you meet him? And why does he think you're engaged?"

"It's a long story, and I'd rather not go into it over the phone. Would you mind if I save it until I see you?"

Jill sighed, but agreed. "I'm going to want every juicy detail," she warned before hanging up.

Maddie swallowed a moan.

The phone rang again two minutes later. It was Mrs. Underwood, a member of Maddie's church who'd known the Carmichael family since before Maddie's birth. "I heard the most exciting news this afternoon," Mrs. Underwood said. "So, you and Jackson have decided to tie the knot, hmm? I must say, I'm surprised. I never would have thought . . . but, still, I didn't like the thought of your haring off to Europe alone."

"I'm not engaged to Jackson," Maddie protested automatically.

"You're not? Then who *are* you engaged to?" Mrs. Underwood asked in blunt surprise.

"I'm not engaged to anyone," Maddie answered, wondering how many times she would have to say those words before the day was over. Mitchell's Fork was a small town and a closely knit one. She knew all too well how quickly news traveled through the gossip lines—she'd left the restaurant less than an hour ago!—and how wildly distorted it could become after a few avid tellings. "This is all a mistake."

"But Sarah Kennedy said she heard from Martha Jean Claypoole that your engagement was announced at the restaurant this afternoon."

"Martha Jean was misinformed," Maddie replied, her voice strained. "I'm sorry, Mrs. Underwood, but I really have to go now. Thank you for calling."

"But—but—"

Mrs. Underwood was still sputtering when Maddie gently set the receiver in its cradle. It was the first time in her life Maddie had ever deliberately hung up on anyone. Something else to blame on Case Brannigan, she thought grimly.

The phone rang again. Maddie groaned loudly, and backed hastily away from it. She couldn't go through that again. Not now. She really needed to think.

She hurried toward the bedroom doorway, nearly tripping over the denim-and-gingham uniform she'd tossed to the floor after exchanging it for a more comfortable T-shirt and shorts. She kicked the garment aside, leaving it lying in a tangled heap that seemed out of place in the otherwise neat room.

She had to get out. She needed time before she had to face Case again.

And she knew she would be facing him again. All too soon.

2

CASE WAS BEGINNING to wonder if Hazel had deliberately led him on a wild-goose chase. He'd been driving for some ten minutes since turning off the main highway, and the only sign of life he'd seen had been cows grazing in the pastures that lined the rutted asphalt road. It was with some relief that he topped a hill and spotted a large farmhouse at the end of the road.

His optimism grew as he approached the house. This was great, he thought, looking around approvingly. Exactly what he'd had in mind when he'd decided to retire to rural America and start living a quiet, normal life.

The farmhouse was a two-story white frame structure with neat black shutters and a full-length front porch complete with a porch swing. There were winding rock pathways, flower beds just coming into spring bloom, white picket fences, a sparkling pond in the distance—even a couple of dogs lolling on the thick, neatly trimmed front lawn. A second, smaller house sat off to one side—a guest house, perhaps, or staff housing.

Straight out of a Norman Rockwell painting, Case thought with a contented nod. Perfect. He would have bet any amount of money that the Maddie Carmichael he'd met in Cancún had grown up in surroundings like this.

He parked in the circular driveway and climbed out of his car. The two dogs ran toward him, barking. It took him only a wary moment to realize that their tails were wagging and that they seemed absolutely delighted to see him. He patted their shaggy heads, and quickly gave up trying to guess their breeds. Both looked like mutts to him. Big, noisy, friendly mutts.

An older woman with almost blinding white hair appeared from behind one corner of the house, thumping a heavy wooden cane against the ground as she walked. She seemed surprised to see Case. "Who are you?"

"My name is Case Brannigan. I'm looking for Maddie."

The woman studied Case from head to toe—he was getting used to being examined like a sideshow exhibit, he thought resignedly. And then she shrugged. "She's probably up in her room. Ring the bell and ask the housekeeper. I have to tend to my rosebushes."

"Don't let me keep you," Case murmured, though the woman had already moved past him. He was a bit bemused as he climbed the three steps to the front porch.

He rang the doorbell twice before the door was opened by a short, rather bowlegged man in a plaid Western-style shirt and faded jeans that sagged beneath a drooping stomach. "What can I do for you?" the man asked.

Judging the guy to be in his mid- to late-forties, Case wondered who he was. A caretaker? The housekeeper's husband, perhaps? "I'm here to see Maddie," he explained.

"Maddie?" The man cocked his head and gave Case the now-familiar once-over. "She's not in."

Case frowned, suspecting that Maddie had given instructions for him to be told that she was gone. Since the elderly woman had already told him she *was* here, he had no intention of meekly leaving. "I was told that she is in," he insisted.

"And I'm telling you she ain't."

Case was beginning to get annoyed. His acquaintances could have warned this guy that it wasn't a good idea to annoy Case Brannigan. "Just who *are* you?" he asked bluntly.

"I'm Frank," the man answered, then added casually, "the housekeeper."

"The, uh, housekeeper's husband?" Case asked, thinking he must have misunderstood.

Frank shook his head. "The housekeeper," he corrected. "You got a problem with that?"

Case was beginning to get a headache. He took a deep breath. "My only problem right now is that I need to talk to Maddie," he said through clenched teeth. "If you'd just tell me where she is, I would really appreciate it."

"You the guy who's telling everyone you're her fiancé?"

Case's eyebrows shot up. "How did you know that?"

Frank shrugged. "Word gets around fast here."

It had been less than an hour since Case had appeared at the restaurant. "One hell of an efficient grapevine," he muttered.

Frank chuckled. "Yeah. So, you are the guy?"

"I'm the guy who's going to marry Maddie Carmichael," Case agreed determinedly.

Frank's grin widened. "Are you, now? Well, from what I hear, you've got to convince Maddie first."

"That's exactly what I intend to do—as soon as I get a chance to talk to her."

"You might try down by the creek," Frank said, seeming to come to some sort of decision. "Follow that path around the end of my house over there and keep going back to the woods. Then just stay on it until you get to the creek. Maddie walks down there sometimes when she wants to do some thinking."

"Thanks," Case said, already moving toward the steps.

"Don't mention it," the unusual housekeeper replied. "I've gotta get back to the kitchen. I've got a cake in the oven that has to come out. Good luck."

"Uh—thanks," Case said again just as Frank closed the door.

"Weird," Case muttered, limping down the path Frank had pointed out. He hoped the creek wasn't very far into the woods. Though he'd recovered most of his former mobility, he wasn't sure he was up to a strenuous hike.

Things weren't going at all as he'd planned when he'd arrived in Mitchell's Fork to claim his woman.

A LATE-MAY BREEZE rippled the surface of the creek, making the water splash against the shiny gray rocks of the creek bed. Overhead, the new spring leaves rustled in that same breeze, casting dancing shadows on the ground below. Sitting on a thick mat of grass, Maddie rested her back against the trunk of a tree, her eyes closed as she listened to the singing of half a dozen varieties of birds and the distant chatter of two playful squirrels.

She usually found peace in these woods. Nature's sedative for overstressed nerves. But she was finding it extremely difficult to relax today. Not even Nature could soothe the anxiety of knowing that Case Brannigan had suddenly reappeared in her life.

"Maddie."

It was without surprise that she heard his voice behind her. She sighed, knowing it had only been a matter of time. She didn't look around when she said, "Please go away."

"No."

Well, it had been worth a shot. She turned her head and looked up at him. He was rather overdressed for a stroll in the woods, dressed as he was in a dark suit, white shirt and tie. He was thinner than she remembered, and there were hollows beneath his eyes that hadn't been there before. Unfortunately, she still found him one of the most ruggedly attractive men she'd ever seen. Not that it mattered anymore, she assured herself hastily.

He took another step toward her and she noticed that he was limping rather badly. What had he done to himself? But, even more important, why was he here?

When she didn't say anything, Case cleared his throat. "You look different," he said.

"So do you."

"I spent a couple of months in a hospital."

She sensed that he expected her to cry out in sympathy and concern. She kept to herself any emotions she might have felt. "Did you?"

He was frowning when he nodded. "Yeah."

"Sorry to hear that."

His frown deepened. "Don't you want to know what happened?"

"Not really."

Case made a sound of frustration and shoved a hand through his hair.

She remembered that he did that often, which was the reason it usually lay tumbled over his forehead, as it was now. She didn't want to remember how endearing she'd found that boyish forelock before; she told herself it didn't particularly appeal to her now.

"What the hell is wrong with you, Maddie?" Case demanded in utterly male exasperation. "Why are you acting like this? Why are you so angry with me? It's not as though I took off without even leaving you a note."

Oh, he'd left a note, all right. *Go home, and wait for me.*

She could still see the scrawled words very clearly in her mind. Just as she could imagine the beautiful redhead with whom she'd been told Case had left the resort. And the look of sympathy in Carmelita's dark eyes when she'd told Maddie about that mysterious other woman.

"I'm not angry with you, Case," she said as coolly as she could manage. "I'm rather grateful to you, actually. You saved us both from an embarrassing scene."

"An embarrassing scene?" he repeated, propping one hand against the trunk of the tree she sat beneath. "You mean, like the one you caused at your restaurant?"

She flushed, but didn't look away from him. "No. That was, um...you caught me by surprise. I was talking about Cancún. Your note saved me the trouble of telling you myself that I'd changed my mind about marrying you."

Case's eyes widened, then narrowed. "What do you mean, you'd changed your mind? You expect me to believe that you wouldn't have married me even if I hadn't been called away?"

Called away—what an interesting way of looking at it. She pushed the lingering bitterness to the back of her mind, determined that he wouldn't hear it in her voice. "That's exactly what I'm saying. I realized that morning that I was making a mistake, letting myself get carried away by...well, by a lot of things. But when it came right down to it, I knew I couldn't impulsively marry a stranger."

A thin white line had appeared around Case's mouth. Maddie focused on it intently. It was easier to look there than to meet his smoldering dark eyes.

"You're saying this to save face, aren't you?" he accused her. "You want me to believe you were the one who called it off."

"Think what you like," she said with a shrug. "It doesn't really matter. The important thing is, we didn't go through with it. Whatever it was...it's over."

"The hell it is."

He spoke with a controlled vehemence that made her instinctively tighten her arms around her upraised knees. She was determined that he wouldn't see any sign that he intimidated her. The new Maddie Carmichael wasn't a meek little mouse like the old one had been. But it was hard not to appear intimidated when she was sitting on the ground and he was looming over her, she decided.

She pushed herself to her feet and faced him squarely. "It's over," she repeated. "Face it, Case, there was never anything all that serious between us. It was a vacation romance, for heaven's sake. An impulsive fling. We never . . . er . . . we didn't even—you know."

"Go to bed together? You're right. I can see now that was a mistake."

She frowned. "What do you mean?"

"If we'd become lovers in Cancún, we wouldn't be having this argument now. You'd know you belonged to me."

His airily confident statement made her gasp in outrage. Of all the unmitigated nerve!

What an idiot she'd been in Cancún, not to see the arrogance behind this man's charm. She'd been so swept away by the sheer romance of the whole situation, so flattered by his single-minded attentions, so besotted with his rugged good looks and overwhelming masculinity that she'd completely ignored the warnings of her better judgment.

She'd actually agreed to marry him! Of course, she'd done so during a hand-in-hand walk on a moonlit beach after an evening of dinner and dancing and subtle seduction. And he'd proposed to her after kissing her until her ears buzzed and her mind was too clouded by desire to conjure even a modicum of common sense.

He'd told her he wanted her. Told her he needed her. That he'd been looking for her for a very long time.

She'd been on a plane back to Mississippi, her pride shredded and her eyes red from crying, before it had occurred to her that he'd never once said he loved her.

Those painful memories made her lift her chin and face him without flinching. "I don't belong to you, Case Brannigan. I don't belong to anyone."

He only quirked one dark eyebrow in an expression that made her long to hit him. The old Maddie would never even have considered such a violent, unladylike impulse. The new one was terribly tempted.

She took a deep, steadying breath, determined to settle this maturely and rationally. "Look, Case, I don't know what you're doing here, I don't know what you want from me, but the fact is, you and I are not engaged. We're practically strangers, for Pete's sake. What happened between us last year was an...an aberration. Too much moonlight, too many slow dances, too much champagne. We both came to our senses the next morning, and I, for one, would like to keep it that way."

"I didn't change my mind the next morning," Case argued. "I was called away. On business."

She didn't quite snort. She thought about it, though.

"As for the rest of what you said, that's pure bull. And I can prove it," he added, his hands falling onto her shoulders.

She stiffened and eyed him suspiciously, much too aware of the warmth of his hands through her T-shirt. "I don't think you—"

"There's no moonlight now," he broke in, jerking his chin to indicate the bright afternoon sun. "I haven't slow-danced in six months, and neither of us has had any champagne."

"I don't know what—"

"Just wanted to make that clear before I did this," he murmured. And then he crushed her mouth beneath his.

Maddie tried to push him away. But somehow, her fingers tangled in his jacket, where they stubbornly remained. She parted her lips to tell him to stop. His tongue swept between them, effectively smothering the words.

And she was lost.

No one had ever kissed her the way Case did. No other man had made her hands tremble, her knees go weak, her mind spin, her skin burn. Until Case had first kissed her six months ago, she'd thought those reactions existed only in fiction. With Case, she'd found the fireworks she'd only ever dreamed of.

She knew without doubt that this was only a mild imitation of the way he would make her feel if they ever progressed beyond kissing.

His hands swept her body, as though reacquainting themselves with her curves, seeking out the changes a strict diet-and-exercise program had wrought. She couldn't help noticing how thin he felt against her.

She tried to ignore the automatic wave of concern that swept through her. She didn't want to know what had happened to him, didn't want to care about how badly he might have suffered. She didn't want to be standing here, kissing him with the hunger of someone who'd been deprived of nourishment for six long months.

She ripped her mouth away from his and lowered her head, gasping for breath and trying desperately to regain her composure.

"No moonlight," Case murmured, his voice rough. "No champagne."

Sometime during the kiss, her bravado had vanished. She closed her eyes and whispered weakly, "Don't do this, Case."

She wasn't sure she could go through this again.

"It's too late, Maddie. You're mine. You have been since I bought you that first drink in Cancún. You'd save us both a lot of trouble if you'd just admit it now."

"I—I . . ." In a surge of panic, she broke away from him and raced blindly away, toward the safety and the privacy of her home.

She heard Case call her name, heard him curse as he stumbled on the rough path, but she didn't slow down. She had to put a safe distance between them, had to recover from the effects of that kiss before the next confrontation.

She just couldn't seem to think when Case kissed her.

CASE TOOK only two running steps after Maddie before he realized that he wasn't going to catch her. This time. He stopped with a muttered curse, jerking impatiently at the knot of his tie. Damn it, nothing was going the way he'd planned!

He forced himself to take a deep breath and calm down. Think logically. Okay, so maybe he'd been rather arrogant to assume that Maddie would welcome him with open arms, and that they'd take up exactly where they'd left off six months ago. Truth was, he'd never even questioned that she would wait for him.

It had come as an ugly shock to him to hear that she had been dating someone else. But whoever the guy was, whatever she'd done, she had still responded to Case's kiss with the same hunger she'd shown in Cancún. Just as he'd felt that same jolt of incredible rightness. A soul-deep recognition that this was the woman he wanted beside him for the rest of his life, no matter how hard she was trying to convince him that she had changed.

Maddie seemed to believe that he'd left Cancún because he'd changed his mind about marrying her. If only there had been time for him to see her, talk to her. She said she'd gotten his note—but obviously, his hastily scrawled message hadn't been sufficient. He hadn't been able to contact her during the past six months—first because he'd been too far out in the wilds of Colombia to contact *anyone* and then because he'd been hospitalized in a foreign country, out of commission and not entirely sure he'd recover enough to marry anyone.

By the time he'd been reassured that he wouldn't be an invalid, known he needn't hesitate to find Maddie again, he'd been so impatient to see her that he couldn't wait for an invitation. He'd tried calling, a week ago. He'd called all the Carmichaels in the area until he'd finally reached someone who'd said yes, Maddie lived there—but she wasn't home. Case hadn't wanted to leave a message. He'd decided he would rather surprise her.

He'd done so, it seemed. And received a few nasty surprises, himself.

He could explain everything—if he could ever get her to sit still long enough to listen, damn it.

He told himself that it was really a good sign that Maddie was so angry. Had she been cool and composed, he might have worried. But he'd seen the tumultuous emotions in her eyes, felt them in her kiss. He knew she was no more indifferent to him now than she had been in Cancún.

He would win, simply because he couldn't bear the thought of losing. Case Brannigan wanted a home, a family. A life.

He fully intended to have those things with Maddie.

MADDIE WAS CURLED on her window seat, staring blindly at her bare feet, when a brisk knock rattled her bedroom door. "Dinner's ready," Aunt Nettie announced, opening the door without waiting for an invitation. "Look at you, girl. Hair all a mess, still wearing your shorts, no shoes. I want you to put on something decent and brush that hair before you come downstairs, you hear? Hurry up now, everyone's waiting for you."

Maddie opened her mouth to say she wasn't hungry. And then she closed it with a swallowed sigh, remembering the occasion. Unfortunately, there was no way she could graciously get out of the family meal this evening. "All right, Aunt Nettie, I'm coming."

"And don't come down looking like a sulled-up possum, either," her great-aunt replied firmly, in exactly the same tone she'd used when Maddie was a toddler. "Frank spent hours cleaning that mess of greens and basting that ham for your grandpa's birthday dinner. He's even made a chocolate cake for dessert. I want you to show him you appreciate his trouble."

"I will, Aunt Nettie," Maddie murmured obediently—exactly as she had when she was a toddler.

Nettie nodded in curt satisfaction and closed the door, but not without urging Maddie one last time to "get a move on."

Maddie changed quickly into a loose-fitting, red knit dress and ran a brush through her hair. She slid her bare feet into comfortable black flats, hoping Nettie wouldn't notice that she wasn't wearing stockings. Nettie Bragg, Mike Carmichael's eighty-year-old paternal aunt, was bossy, opinionated, tactless and impatient. But Maddie loved her dearly.

She paused to pull a brightly wrapped present out of her closet before heading downstairs. Today was Grampa Carmichael's eighty-ninth birthday and the evening would be a festive one. Maddie had no intention of allowing Case Brannigan to ruin that for her. She would simply put him out of her mind, she told herself as she marched downstairs toward the sounds of chattering voices drifting from the dining room. She wouldn't even think about Case Brannigan for the rest of the...

And then she saw him. Case was standing in the dining room, surrounded by her obviously avidly curious family. He met her eyes and smiled, looking as though he planned to stay right where he was for the rest of the evening.

So much for putting him out of her mind, she thought with a mental groan.

3

MIKE CARMICHAEL WAS the first person other than Case to notice his daughter's entrance. "Here's Maddie now," he announced, stepping toward her with a quizzical look. "Come in, honey. Maybe you'd like to formally introduce us to your, er, fiancé."

The quick glare Maddie gave Case should have singed his eyebrows. He only smiled blandly.

"What is he doing here?" Maddie asked her father.

Mike seemed to be fighting a grin. "Well, he was just sort of hanging around outside, so I invited him in," her father admitted. "He's a stranger in our town, honey. We don't want him to think we aren't hospitable, now, do we?"

"I don't really care what he thinks," Maddie replied. "This is a family dinner."

"According to Case, here, he's about to become part of the family," Mike returned, obviously enjoying the confusion.

Maddie's hands drew into fists, but she took a deep breath to calm herself before speaking. "I'm afraid Mr. Brannigan has been teasing you, Dad," she said firmly. "He isn't my fiancé. He's merely an acquaintance."

Lounging nearby, apparently completely at ease, Case laughed softly. "Is that what I am?" he murmured, unfazed by the description.

Maddie realized that his comfortable reaction had the effect of making her look like the one who wasn't being quite honest. "Yes," she said flatly. "That's *all*."

She turned away to set her grandfather's present on a low side table already piled with other gifts, needing a few moments to recuperate from her surprise at finding Case here. Maybe then she'd know how to handle this without causing an unpleasant scene that could only lead to further embarrassment for her.

Aunt Nettie was watching her closely; Maddie avoided the old woman's too-perceptive eyes as she passed, heading for the man seated at the head of the long dining table.

She leaned over and planted a kiss on the elderly man's bald head. "Happy birthday, Grampa."

The doorbell rang before her grandfather could answer. He beamed. "More guests for my party," he announced, his frail face lighting with pleasure. Grampa Carmichael loved being the center of attention, Maddie thought with an indulgent smile.

The new arrivals were more members of the family. Mike's sister, Anita, and her husband, Dan, were accompanied by their daughter, Maddie's cousin, Lisa, who was five years older than Maddie and had been divorced for several years. Lisa's fifteen-year-old twins, Kathy and Jeff, trailed into the room behind her.

The room was getting full, and everyone seemed to be talking at once. Yet Maddie was constantly aware of Case, standing slightly to one side of the room, watching everything that went on yet never really taking his attention from her.

She heard her father introducing Case to his sister. "This is Case Brannigan," Mike said. "He claims to be Maddie's fiancé."

Maddie flushed as her aunt Anita exclaimed in surprise. This was really getting awkward, she seethed. And her father was behaving almost as badly as Case.

She should have known Mike would find this whole thing amusing; she'd always accused her father of having a warped sense of humor, a charge he'd never been able to deny. She loved him dearly, but this wasn't the first time he'd put her on the spot with his love of a good joke.

Obviously, he'd decided Case wasn't a threat to her; Mike could be fiercely overprotective of his only child when he chose. So why did he seem to be welcoming Case with open arms? Maddie fumed.

"You're marrying this guy, Maddie?" Kathy asked with typical teenage bluntness. "I thought you were dating that cute Jackson Babbit."

"Jackson Babbit's a jerk," Jeff pronounced scornfully. "The guy wears enough hair spray to choke a gopher, and those weird clothes—" He shuddered expressively.

"Kathy, Jeff, please," their mother murmured in exasperation. "This is none of your business."

Maddie turned to Lisa's twins, intending to gently reinforce her cousin's words, but she was quickly distracted. "Jeff!" she gasped, seeing the boy closely for the first time that evening. "What happened to your face?"

Jeff flushed behind his bruises and shrugged. "Nothing," he muttered.

"Danny Cooper beat him up," Kathy said, planting her fists on her slender hips, her dark eyes sparking. "Him and that gang of creeps he hangs out with."

"Shut up, Kathy," Jeff grumbled, obviously uncomfortable that the attention in the crowded room had suddenly shifted to him.

"Something is going to have to be done about that Cooper boy and his gang before someone is seriously hurt," Anita said, her distress showing as she studied her grandson's battered face. "I just don't understand why Sheriff McAdams won't do anything about them."

"Same reason Mayor Sloane ain't saying anything about it," Nettie observed cynically. "The Cooper money put both of them in office and the Cooper money's keeping them there. That Cooper boy's just as mean and power-hungry as his daddy is, and ain't nobody around here got the guts to do anything about it."

"I wanted to go have a talk with Major Cooper, but Lisa talked me out of it," Maddie's uncle Dan, Jeff's devoted grandfather, insisted.

"I just didn't want any more trouble with the Coopers," Lisa said, looking harried. She turned to Maddie. "Danny Cooper's already making Jeff's life hell. If we start anything with his family, who knows what kind of revenge Danny and those other boys will take?"

Maddie was aware that Case had been listening to every word of the family exchange, a deep frown creasing his forehead. "One teenage boy is terrorizing this entire town?" he asked Mike as though he couldn't quite believe what he was hearing.

Mike nodded grimly. "Pretty much," he admitted. "His father terrorized the town twenty years ago, and his father before that. You might say it's a tradition around these parts. Problem is, each generation gets meaner and more blatant about it."

"And nobody will do anything to stop it?"

The adults in the room sighed. "Major Cooper is the third-generation owner of a manufacturing plant that employs a good fifty percent of the citizens of Mitchell's Fork," Mike explained. "Which makes it...difficult for most folks around here to get involved. So far, the boys haven't done anything too drastic—"

"Beating up my grandson isn't drastic?" Anita demanded.

"C'mon, Grandma, it wasn't that bad," Jeff muttered, still embarrassed.

Anita shook her head, but subsided.

"So when are you guys getting married?" Jeff asked Maddie, motioning toward Case. It was an obvious ploy to divert attention—and it succeeded.

"Yes, Maddie," Mike said blandly, his eyes lighting again. "When *are* you guys getting married?"

Maddie tossed her artfully gold-streaked hair, sending it swinging around her face. "When hell freezes over," she said succinctly.

Nettie gasped. "Madelyn Kathleen Carmichael! You watch your mouth, you hear? There are innocent ears in this room," she scolded, looking meaningfully toward Kathy and Jeff.

Case only grinned. "She'll come around," he assured Jeff. "She's just a little annoyed with me at the moment."

Maddie gasped in outrage. Annoyed? *Annoyed?* She opened her mouth to set him straight, but Jeff was already speaking. "Yeah?" he asked Case curiously. "How come?"

Case shrugged. "Let's just say we've had a breakdown in communication."

"What's this about Maddie getting married?" Grampa Carmichael demanded, as usual a bit slower than the others in catching the topic of discussion.

Maddie barely resisted throwing up her hands in a gesture of frustration and screeching. This was getting to be too much for her to handle. She would never be able to explain everything to Grampa at the moment...that would take some time and prove extremely embarrassing in front of everyone. "Never mind, Grampa," she said, hoping he would take the hint.

But Case had already stepped forward and was introducing himself to the family patriarch. "Case Brannigan," he said, extending a large, callused hand.

Grampa Carmichael took the hand in his own trembling, age-spotted one. His faded eyes searched Case's face, and he frowned when he didn't recognize the features. "You aren't from around here, are you?"

"No, sir. But I plan to hang around a while. This looks like a good place to put down roots."

Grampa nodded. "Lived here all my life," he said proudly. "Raised the kids here. Now we got a fourth generation going," he added, motioning toward Jeff and Kathy. "Maddie's almost thirty, you know. Been telling her it's time she settled down and had herself some kids."

Maddie groaned. It looked as though she was going to have to explain, after all. Everyone was watching her so intently. She guessed she couldn't blame them. It was certainly unusual for Maddie to be the one to cause a family scene. "Grampa, Case isn't really my fiancé," she began.

"Oh?" Grampa looked from Case's bland expression to Maddie's harried one. "Well, what is he, then?"

Everyone seemed to expect Maddie to answer that one, including Case. "He's—he's—" *What? A friend? A vacation acquaintance? A total stranger?* None of the descriptions seemed quite adequate.

"Well?" Grampa prodded impatiently. "Did you agree to marry this man or didn't you?"

Case smiled. "Tell him, Maddie," he urged. "What was your answer when I proposed to you on that beach in Cancún?"

Maddie opened her mouth, then closed it, feeling trapped. "Er—"

Nettie cocked her white-haired head and thumped the floor with her cane. "Tell us what's going on, Madelyn," she insisted. "*Did* you tell this man you'd marry him?"

"Yes!" Maddie said in exasperation. "But—"

Case's smile deepened in satisfaction. "If I hadn't been called away on business, Maddie would already be my wife," he said. "We were going to be married in Cancún."

"And you never said a word about this to anyone?" Mike asked. The humor had faded from his mischievous eyes, to be replaced by a touch of hurt. He and Maddie had been very close since her mother died five years ago; Maddie knew Mike was wondering why she hadn't shared this with him.

She couldn't have explained, even now. She simply hadn't been able to talk about Case, or about her humiliation when she'd stood in that little room, reading that curt note in front of pitying strangers.

"Dad, I'm sorry," she murmured. "I'll explain later. I promise."

Mike nodded and gave her a smile, but it was a strained one. Perhaps, she thought, he had only just realized that Case hadn't been carrying on an elaborate practical joke when he'd appeared and introduced himself as Maddie's fiancé. Mike must have suddenly understood that Maddie really *had* agreed to become Case's wife, and would have already done so had something not happened to prevent it.

Maddie could understand why her father looked so startled by the realization; she was finding it hard to believe, herself, that she'd come so close to making such a huge mistake. Thank goodness that fate, in the form of a tall redhead, had stepped in to stop her, she thought fervently.

"Seems to me," Grampa Carmichael said slowly, "that if a woman gives her word to a man, she's bound to uphold it."

Maddie's cousin Lisa sighed and shook her head. "Talk about a generation gap," she whispered.

"Seems to me," Nettie said, not to be left out, "that this young woman gave her word too fast. Imagine, agreeing to marry a man you just met," she said with a disapproving shake of her head.

Maddie almost sighed in relief to have finally found an ally.

But then Nettie spoiled it by shaking an arthritic finger at Case. "Our Maddie deserves a proper courtship," she told him. "Ain't no need to go rushing anything. You do it right this time, you hear?"

"I'm willing to give her a little time," Case conceded. "But I'm holding her to her word."

Maddie whirled on him. "Case, you cannot just—"

"If I were you," Uncle Dan said thoughtfully, as though Maddie weren't even there, "I'd slow down a bit, boy. Take her to the movies. Send her flowers. That's the way I courted Anita, here, nearly forty years ago. I believe the procedure is about the same these days."

"Uncle Dan," Maddie began.

"These days, the woman's likely to do the asking, and the paying," Jeff said cheekily, getting his grandmother's full attention.

Anita lifted a thinly plucked dark eyebrow. "A lady doesn't ask a man for a date. And any man who would let a woman pay for their dinner is hardly a gentleman."

"Mother," Lisa said loudly with a roll of her eyes. "Was that a dig about Charlie? Just because I loaned him a few dollars, you and Daddy are convinced he's a gigolo. He's really a very nice guy," she insisted. "The first one I've really liked since Bill and I got divorced."

"A real man doesn't take loans from his lady friends," Anita insisted. Maddie's problems were suddenly forgotten as Anita turned her attention to her own daughter's worrisome love life.

Nettie was moving to intercede between mother and daughter before a quarrel developed. Maddie stepped aside to allow her great-aunt to pass, relieved that at least three of her family members had decided to leave her—and her love life—alone for the moment. "Anita, you let the girl be," Nettie ordered. "She's old enough to know her own mind now."

"But she—"

"I met my blushing bride on a Mississippi riverboat," Grampa mused out loud, not addressing anyone in particular. "It was a fine day. A Saturday, as I remember. Annabelle was wearing a floating white dress and carrying—"

Because everyone in the room, except Case, of course, had heard the story many times, no one paid much attention to the elderly man's ramblings.

Maddie took advantage of the confusion—and the merciful distraction—to take Case firmly by the arm. "I want to see you outside," she said through gritted teeth. "*Now.*"

With rather suspicious ease, Case allowed her to all but drag him from the room.

"YOUR FAMILY IS very interesting," Case said as soon as they'd stepped out onto the long porch of the family farmhouse. "They certainly don't hesitate to speak their minds, do they?"

"No, they don't. Or to butt into another family member's business," Maddie agreed grimly, still seething over all the advice Case had been given on the proper way to "court" her.

"I suppose that's common with large, close families."

"Probably. Case, I—"

"I can get used to it," he said with a decisive nod of his head.

Maddie was exasperated at the arrogance of his magnanimous concession. "Oh, you can, can you?"

"Sure. That's just the way families are." He seemed oddly satisfied with the conclusion.

Maddie had lost the thread of the conversation somewhere. She struggled to regain control of it. "Case, we need to talk."

"Yes." He crossed his arms over his chest and leaned against a porch post, one foot up on the railing behind him. He breathed deeply of the crisp, spring evening air and his gaze wandered over the moon-washed rural surroundings. "You have a nice home here, Maddie. It's no wonder you haven't been in any hurry to leave it."

She was glad for the shadows that partially concealed her when she felt her cheeks wash with color. She'd become increasingly sensitive lately about still living at home with her family. But then, she'd become increasingly sensitive about a lot of things during the past six months.

"I lived on my own for a while after I finished college," she said casually. "Had an apartment in town, close to the restaurant. I moved back here a couple of years ago, when Aunt Nettie broke her hip and the last housekeeper retired. After my trip to Europe, I plan to start looking for a new place, now that everything seems to be going smoothly here again."

Case started to say something, but hesitated. When he spoke, she sensed he'd deliberately changed the topic. "Speaking of housekeepers, I met yours earlier."

"Frank?"

"Yeah. He wasn't exactly what I expected."

She couldn't resist a slight smile. "I know. But he's wonderful. He runs the household so smoothly that I don't know what we'd do without him now."

"How did you find him?"

"He was in the service with Dad many years ago. Dad had always told him that if he ever needed a job to look him up. Of course, Dad was thinking of giving him a job at the restaurant—Frank was a cook in the army. A few months after the last housekeeper left and I moved back in, Frank showed up on the doorstep and told Dad he'd lost his job and his wife and he wanted to take Dad up on his offer."

"His wife died?" Case asked in sympathy.

"No. She ran off with a traveling evangelist."

"Oh," he said blankly.

Maddie nodded. "Anyway, almost before anyone knew how it happened, he had moved into the guest house and taken over the running of the household. He cooks, cleans, does the shopping, takes care of Grampa, makes sure Aunt Nettie takes her medicine—he's probably the most important member of the family," she concluded with a chuckle.

"Your family seems eager to welcome new members," Case said carefully, still looking out at the misty lawn.

Maddie thought she detected a touch of wistfulness in his deep voice. And then she told herself she must be mistaken. Case Brannigan wasn't deceiving her with this lonely-little-orphan routine. She didn't know what he was after, exactly, but this time she had no intention of making a fool of herself over him.

"Case," she said, dropping all pretense of casual conversation. "Why are you here?"

He turned his head to look at her. "I'm here to claim my wife."

His equally blunt words sent a quiver through her. She had to clear her throat before she could speak coolly. "You don't have a wife. At least, not that I know of. Unless, of course, you married the redhead."

He blinked. "Redhead?" he repeated.

She shrugged. "I heard you left with a tall, beautiful redhead. Your boss, I suppose?"

Case suddenly smiled, his teeth ferally white in the shadows. "Is *that* what this is about? You thought I'd dumped you for another woman? Maddie, you—"

He took an impulsive step toward her. She backed away hastily, holding both hands up to ward him off. "Don't touch me," she warned, trying not to sound as desperate as she felt. If he kissed her again now... "I don't want you to touch me, Case."

He sighed, but remained where he was. "It wasn't what it looked like, Maddie."

"I don't care."

"Of course you do." His gently indulgent tone set her teeth on edge. Now he'd convinced himself that this whole thing was a case of wounded feminine pride, she realized in frustration.

"I *don't* care," she repeated very distinctly. "It doesn't matter to me why you left. The important thing is, we didn't go through with it. I'm not your wife, thank God, and I never will be."

"You gave me your word, Maddie."

"And you gave me yours!" she snapped before she could stop herself. "I was there. Where the hell were *you?*"

She snapped her mouth shut, but realized it was too late. She'd already as much admitted that she hadn't changed her mind that morning in Cancún. Damn it.

"Are you aware," Case said quietly, "that this is the first time you asked me why I wasn't there?"

She tried frantically to regain her composure. "That's because I don't particularly care why you weren't there," she said airily. "I'm only glad you saved me from making a huge mistake."

"It wouldn't have been a mistake. And it won't be a mistake this time."

"There *is* no this time. It's over. I'm not going to let you charm me this time, Brannigan. I have plans, and I'm not changing them just because you've suddenly shown up again."

"We'll talk about those plans of yours later—among other things," Case said a bit ominously. "First, I'm going to tell you why I had to leave you in Cancún. And you're going to listen, damn it."

She decided she might as well humor him for now. And besides, she really wanted to hear this explanation. How *did* he intend to explain the tall redhead? His sister? He'd better not try that one!

She crossed her arms in a deliberate imitation of him and leaned against the wall behind her. "Fine," she said. "Let's hear it."

He didn't look particularly pleased with her attitude, but he let it go. "I told you I worked for the government," he began.

"Yes. I suppose that was a fantasy, too?"

"*Damn it,* Maddie!" Case stopped and drew a deep breath. "Just be quiet and listen, will you?" he said more quietly.

More shaken by his violent outburst than she wanted him to see, Maddie swallowed and nodded.

He continued with obviously strained patience. "It wasn't a fantasy. I work—I worked for the government. DEA—Drug Enforcement. It's a thankless, dangerous job, but I enjoyed it. For a time. When I met you, I was on leave. I was tired, burned-out. Ready for a change. I went to Cancún for a vacation, and to decide what to do with the rest of my life. But I told you some of this then."

She nodded. She'd believed him then. Later, she'd wondered if it had all been lies. Now . . . now she just didn't know what to believe.

"Anyway," he went on when she remained silent, "Jade—the redhead—"

Of *course* her name was Jade, Maddie thought in despair.

"Jade was a business associate," Case explained. "Another agent. She and I didn't work together often, and didn't get along particularly well when we did. She showed up in Cancún to tell me that my former partner—and one of the only close friends I've ever had—had been captured by drug dealers in the Colombian jungle and was being held as a political hostage. Someone had to go get him—and I was the best they had."

He said the words without bragging, so matter-of-factly that Maddie couldn't help accepting them. She didn't question that Case had been the best at whatever he'd done; she'd learned firsthand that he could be amazingly persistent when he set his mind to something. Convincing her to marry him, for example. "What happened?" she asked, intrigued despite her resistance.

"I got him out," Case said grimly. "Not exactly in the same shape he'd been in before. He's still in rehab. Probably will be for a few months yet. But he's alive."

Maddie looked down at Case's legs, thinking of the limp he'd developed since she'd seen him last. "You were injured." Her voice wasn't quite as steady as she would have liked.

"Yes. There was some doubt at first whether I would walk again." His voice was curiously uninflected.

She caught her breath, but remained silent.

"I couldn't contact you, Maddie—at first because I was out in the jungle tracking down my friend, and then because I was hospitalized in serious condition. I couldn't—I didn't want to call you until I knew I wouldn't be an invalid. I wouldn't have come to you in a wheelchair," he added stiffly. "But I never stopped thinking of you, I swear it. As far as I was concerned, our engagement was on hold, not over. As soon as I'd recovered sufficiently, I came for you. I called once, but you weren't home—so I decided to surprise you."

"You did that," Maddie murmured, trying to take in everything he'd told her.

Could she possibly believe him? He'd told his story simply, without embellishment, but there was a heavy undercurrent in his flat voice. Regret. Bitterness. Pain.

Whatever had happened, he'd suffered. And her heart twisted for him. But she couldn't give in that easily. She kept thinking of the things he *hadn't* said.

"Why do you want to marry me, Case?"

He seemed to stumble for a moment, searching for an answer. "I realized when I met you in Cancún that I had grown tired of the life I'd been leading. I told you I had no family, that I grew up in foster homes and institutions after my mother died when I was seven. I never even knew who my father was. I went into law enforcement when I was still a teenager and spent the last fifteen years on the move, never in one place long enough to put down roots, never sure I would live through the next assignment. I don't want to live that way anymore. I'm ready to settle down, start a family. With you."

She couldn't speak for a moment. A large lump had settled in her throat, blocking whatever words she might have found.

Apparently taking her silence as a signal for him to continue, Case made a sweeping motion with one hand. "I like what I've seen of your town, your family. This looks like a great place to raise kids. We can find a place of our own—a house and some land. I have money, enough to support us until I find a new source of income, and—"

"Case," Maddie broke in swiftly, desperately. She couldn't listen to any more, couldn't hold on to her composure much longer. "Stop, please. Nothing has changed. I'm not marrying you."

"Maddie—"

His voice was liquid seduction. She steeled herself against it.

"No," she said sharply. "Don't. I won't fall back into your arms this time. You look at me and you see a convenient little woman to play house with you and bear your children. Well, forget it. I want a life. I'll be thirty in a few months and I've been away from this town you find so attractive only once."

She stopped only long enough to draw a deep, shaky breath. "Maybe you're tired of excitement and adventure," she said, "but I'm ready to find some of it. I'm going to travel through Europe, try new things, live on the edge. I want to see Ireland and Greece and Portugal and the Czech Republic, all the places I've read about but never thought I'd visit. And not just the tourist stops—I want to go into the villages, the countryside, the places where the real natives live. And then maybe...maybe I'll take up mountain climbing. Or skydiving. Something really adventurous. And I'm going to do it *alone*."

Case was shaking his head. "You don't know what you're saying. Those countries aren't safe for a single woman to explore alone, especially a woman who's only left her safe, secure small town once. You can't just blithely wander into foreign villages where you don't know the language or the customs, hoping you'll be as safe there as you are in Mitchell's Fork. Trust me, Maddie, I've lived that so-called adventurous life you're fantasizing about. You'd hate it. It's not what you want, not what you need."

"*I'll* decide what I want, and what I need," she snapped. "I don't need you to tell me."

"I *am* telling you," he retorted, his own temper starting to fray. "You're a damned lucky woman, Maddie Carmichael. You have a family who loves you, friends, a home. You wake up every morning knowing there's a good chance you'll live to see the end of the day. You don't have to constantly look over your shoulder, wondering who's holding a knife poised at your back. You have it all here. Why would you want to walk away from it?"

"That's just something I'll have to figure out for myself, isn't it?"

"If you want adventure, you can damned well find it with me," he said.

His incredible arrogance both amazed and infuriated her. "What is it going to take to convince you that it's over between us?"

His hands fell heavily onto her shoulders. "Nothing will convince me of that," he said roughly. "I've waited too long for you, Maddie Carmichael. I'm not going to give you up so easily."

"You—"

Her angry words were smothered by his mouth on hers.

4

SOMETIME DURING that long, heated kiss, Maddie realized that she would never be able to convince Case that she wasn't still attracted to him. That she didn't still want him.

She was. And she did. It was all she could do not to drag him behind the nearest bush when he kissed her—which was why she'd been trying to avoid this.

Just as Case finally, reluctantly, released her mouth, she came up with a desperate plan.

"All right," she said, jerking herself out of his arms with such haste that she almost toppled backward. "I can't convince you to go away, so I won't even try."

"Does this mean the engagement is still on?" Case asked warily.

"No." Her answer was unequivocal. "It simply means I can't make you leave Mitchell's Fork. Obviously, you have every right to be here. I'd be willing to bet, however, that within a few weeks, you'll be so bored you'll run screaming for that excitement and adventure you claim you no longer want."

"And I would bet that you're wrong," Case retorted smoothly. "But what about us? Are you going to keep running every time you see me?"

"I," she said, "am going to go on with my life. I have a great deal of responsibility here, and I intend to honor that obligation. But, as soon as I know Dad can get by without me for a while—probably another four or five months, at the most—I'm taking the money I inherited from my mother's parents and I'm going to Europe. Alone."

"Don't waste your money on that bet. It isn't going to happen." Case spoke very softly, but there was implicit challenge in every syllable. "If you want to go to Europe, you'll be going with me."

Maddie opened her mouth to argue, but before she could speak, the front door opened.

"Maddie?" Her father stood in the doorway, looking curiously from Maddie to Case. "Grampa's getting eager to open his presents," he said. "Everyone's waiting for you."

Maddie pushed her hair out of her face and turned toward the door. "I'm coming."

Case moved to follow her. She spun on one heel. "Hold it."

Case hesitated. "Are you asking me to leave?"

"No. My father invited you to join us for dinner and I won't be so ungracious as to renege on the invitation. There is one condition, however."

He sighed and nodded. "No mention of our engagement."

"Our nonexistent engagement," she corrected.

Case only gave her a bland smile. "Whatever you say, Maddie."

She thought briefly of smacking him right across his arrogant, all-too-talented mouth. And then, she decided seethingly, she really should do the same to her father, who was grinning like a mule eating cactus, as Aunt Nettie would say.

"Shut up," she muttered, passing her father with a defiantly lifted chin.

"I didn't say a word," he assured her.

"You didn't have to," she answered with a long-suffering sigh.

TRUE TO HIS WORD, Case was on his best behavior during dinner. He chatted easily with Mike and Uncle Dan, listened attentively to Grampa's ramblings, talked cars and motorcycles with Jeff and blatantly charmed Anita, Lisa and Kathy. As though sensing that Nettie wouldn't be so easily beguiled, he treated her with a respectful deference that quickly won her approval.

Everyone seemed impressed that Case had been a DEA agent. Mike, Dan and Nettie approved of anyone who enforced the law and made an effort to fight the illegal drug trade. Anita, Lisa and Kathy were drawn to the romantic illusion of a dashing government agent, risking his life for the safety of law-abiding citizens.

Jeff, of course, thought Case Brannigan was about the coolest guy he'd ever met.

By the time Frank set the glowing birthday cake on the table for dessert, Maddie was glumly aware that everyone in the room thought she was crazy for continuing to deny her engagement to Case. She could almost hear them thinking that it wasn't as though she'd had any more exciting offers.

In deference to Grampa's limited breath, Frank had placed only one candle in the center of the massive chocolate cake. Grampa blew it out proudly, then beamed as everyone sang "Happy Birthday"—even Case.

The presents were brought over and opened with great ceremony. Grampa acted as delighted by the practical underwear he received from his sister, Nettie, as he was by the expensive, deliciously soft cashmere sweater Dan and Anita had bought him. He seemed especially touched by Maddie's gift. The watercolor she'd painted had been taken from an old photograph of Grampa and Grandma Carmichael on a picnic. Grampa had been dashingly dressed in a crisp, high-collared shirt, suspenders and a straw boater, while his beloved Annabelle wore a lace-trimmed muslin dress and a flower-bedecked straw hat to shade her fair complexion from the sun.

"I remember this day so clearly," Grampa said wistfully, holding the little framed painting between gnarled, trembling hands. "Thank you, Maddie, girl."

Maddie leaned over to kiss his lined cheek. "You're welcome, Grampa. I'm glad you like it."

"It's very good, Maddie," Case said a few minutes later, while the others chattered around them. "I didn't realize you were such a talented artist."

She flushed. "Thank you. But it's just a hobby."

The doorbell chimed softly from another part of the house. Frank held up a hand when Maddie automatically moved to answer it. "You stay put," he said, already moving out of the room. "I'll get it."

Jeff had already lost interest in the birthday party. He turned back to Case. "Were you chasing drug dealers when you hurt your leg, Case?"

"I guess you could say that," Case replied after a slight hesitation.

"Were you shot?"

Again, Case paused, throwing a quick, questioning look at Maddie. When she didn't intercede, he nodded. "Yeah. I was shot. In the back, and my left thigh."

Maddie felt the breath leave her lungs in a hard rush. She hadn't allowed herself to dwell on how Case had been hurt, how he'd ended up in that hospital. Hearing him say the words so bluntly caused a sharp pain to rip through her, almost in sympathy with the agony he must have felt. *Shot. Oh, God.*

She hoped she kept her reactions from her face. She was aware that everyone in the room seemed to be watching her. Everyone except Jeff, who was still utterly fascinated with Case. "Did you ever shoot anyone?" he asked avidly.

"Jeff," his mother and grandmother both murmured repressively.

Everyone else seemed to be waiting for Case's answer. Maddie understood, of course. Case Brannigan was definitely a novelty in these parts. An exotic, rare animal striding through an ordinary barnyard. No one in this room had ever met a government agent before, a man who'd seen the world, risked his life, lived adventures the people of Mitchell's Fork experienced only through movies and daydreams.

Maddie, for one, was tired of living vicariously through Hollywood adventures. She was ready for a few adventures of her own. She didn't know what, exactly, she wanted to do—but she knew she wanted to do something. Something daring. Something bold.

Something the old Maddie Carmichael would never have considered.

"If you don't mind," Case said quietly to Jeff, "I think I'll let that question pass. There were many parts of my job that I didn't enjoy, and don't care to dwell on. Let's just say I did what I had to do, okay, sport?"

Which, of course, answered Jeff's question quite effectively.

"Well," a new male voice said from the doorway. "Isn't this interesting. Who's the dangerous stranger, Maddie?"

Maddie gasped and whirled. "Jackson!" she said, suddenly remembering why he was here. "Oh, heavens."

Jackson Babbit lifted a quizzical dark eyebrow in response to her flustered greeting. Thirty-three years old, twice-divorced, Jackson was considered the local playboy—a reputation he'd rightfully acquired. A successful farm equipment salesman, he liked to pattern himself after popular country-western star Marty Stuart. Jackson wore his near-black hair longish and painstakingly styled, moussed and sprayed so that not a lock was out of place. He favored flashy clothes—like the bright red shirt, tight black pants and highly polished, elaborately stitched Western boots he was wearing now—and expensive jewelry. A gold chain glinted at his throat, and two diamond rings sparkled from his manicured hands.

Jackson was vain and shallow and materialistic, but he was more fun than anyone Maddie had ever dated from Mitchell's Fork. He knew how to laugh, how to play, how to give a woman his complete, undivided attention—if only for a short while. Maddie had been out with him several times in the past three or four months, and she'd thoroughly enjoyed each date. She'd never intended their dates to be more than a pleasant diversion—and maybe a way to shock the town a bit, since no one had ever thought her the type of woman to catch Jackson's wandering eye. Which, of course, she hadn't been before she'd returned from Cancún a changed woman.

She'd made it abundantly clear to Jackson that she was leaving town soon and had no intention of going to bed with him first. He had good-naturedly retorted that he would do everything he could to change her mind before she left, but he'd never done anything that had made her uncomfortable.

Maddie had sensed that Jackson rather enjoyed having an easy, uncomplicated friendship with a woman without the demands of a sexual relationship—something that must be a novelty for him. Of course, she was sure he would heatedly deny the suggestion if she should ever voice her suspicion aloud. After all, he had his hard-earned reputation to consider.

"Jackson," she said again. "I—um—"

"Don't tell me you forgot our date," he said chidingly, his dark eyes glinting with devilish amusement.

She had, actually. She and Jackson had planned to take in a late movie after Grampa's birthday party. How had it completely slipped her mind? As though she even had to ask, she mused ruefully, glancing sideways at Case.

Case was glaring at Jackson with a scowl that should have disintegrated the other man where he stood. It was, quite obviously, loathing at first sight. Maddie gulped.

Jackson didn't seem to notice the antagonism directed his way. He flashed one of his high-voltage smiles, nodded a friendly greeting that included everyone he knew in the room, then stepped toward Case with an outstretched hand. "I don't believe we've met," he said blandly. "I'm Jackson Babbit. And you are...?"

Case barely touched Jackson's hand with his own. "Case Brannigan. Maddie's—"

"Friend," Maddie said quickly, loudly.

"Fiancé," Case finished succinctly.

Jackson's dimples deepened. "It seems we have a difference of opinion here."

"A temporary condition," Case assured him.

"*Very* temporary," Maddie asserted, giving Case a glare of challenge.

Some men might have been daunted by the tension between Maddie and Case. Jackson only grinned more broadly. "Well, Maddie," he said. "How about it? Is our date still on?"

She tossed her head. "Of course it is. I'm ready to go."

"Maddie," Case growled, taking a step toward her.

She met his eyes squarely. It took more courage than she would admit to face the rather dangerous temper growing in his narrowed gray eyes. "Yes, Case?"

He must have been aware, as she was, that there was nothing he could do now, in front of her family. Their gazes held for a long, taut moment in which no one in the room moved. And then Case backed down, reluctantly. "I'll talk to you tomorrow."

She just managed not to exhale in relief. "Maybe," she said with an airiness she was far from feeling.

She quickly kissed her grandfather, said good-night to the others as a group, slipped her hand beneath Jackson's arm and all but dragged him from the room.

In the hallway outside the dining room, she paused for a moment to remember how to breathe again. She could hear snatches of the conversation resuming in the room she'd left, all seemingly centered on her.

"Don't know what's gotten into that girl lately," Nettie grumbled. "She—"

"I don't know what she sees in that Babbit boy," Anita exclaimed. "Why, he—"

"I like her new hairstyle," Kathy mused inconsequentially. "I wonder if—"

"How come you didn't just bash his teeth in, Case?" That, of course, was from Jeff.

"Jeff! Honestly, what am I—" His mother chided him with long-suffering exasperation.

"Maddie?" Jackson asked patiently. "Are you ready to go?"

"Yes, Jackson. Please." She didn't like the hint of desperation in her voice, but she had to get out of there. Immediately.

TO MADDIE'S intense relief, Jackson didn't even mention Case during the short drive to the movie theater. The film they'd selected was a comedy, starring two actors who topped Maddie's list of favorites. She was able to put the stressful events of the day out of her mind, for the most part, and enjoy the silliness on screen. A two-hour escape from worrying about the confrontation awaiting her the next day.

A couple of fast-food restaurants were the only local establishments open after the late movie on that Sunday evening. Jackson pulled into the parking lot of the Dairy Queen. "Want some ice cream?" he asked.

"Sure. Why not?" She'd been on a strict low-fat diet since returning from Cancún, but tonight she felt like splurging. After all, she hadn't been able to eat more than a bite of birthday cake earlier, not with Case and her family watching her so closely.

Jackson ordered banana splits and coffee for both of them. Maddie didn't bother to point out that he hadn't asked what she wanted. He did things like that all the time, and though Maddie didn't usually let him get away with it, tonight she was too distracted to protest.

"So," he said, as soon as they were seated with their desserts, "tell me about Case Brannigan. Why does he think he's your fiancé?"

"Probably because I said I would marry him," Maddie muttered.

Jackson didn't even blink. "That might have led him to reach certain conclusions."

She had to smile at his dry comment. "I know. But I changed my mind."

"Certainly a woman's prerogative—or a man's, for that matter."

"The problem is that Case apparently hasn't changed his. Even though he left me standing at the altar in Cancún, damn it. I don't know if the redhead really is just a business associate or if she was more—and I really don't care, of course—but I won't be a convenient little woman for some burned-out ex-spy coming in out of the cold. He's got this really strange, idealized image of small-town life, probably because he never really had a family or anything, and I certainly don't blame him for wanting one, but if he thinks I'm just going to give up all my dreams and all my plans to set up housekeeping with him, even though he's never even said—"

Suddenly aware that Jackson was quietly eating his ice cream and listening attentively to every rambled word, Maddie stopped and flushed. "I'm sorry," she said. "I know that diatribe couldn't have made much sense."

"On the contrary. I found it very enlightening."

Maddie winced. "Um—"

"So, you aren't going to marry him?"

"No." She spoke a bit too quickly.

"I don't know, Maddie. He looked like the persistent type to me."

"I can be persistent, myself," she insisted. "Trust me, in a few weeks, Case will be so bored with Mitchell's Fork that he'll be begging to escape. You know what it's like around here, Jackson. You've said yourself that you'd leave if you hadn't worked so hard to make your business a success."

Jackson shrugged, a bit sheepishly. "Mitchell's Fork is okay. A little slow, but I do my best to liven it up occasionally."

Maddie frowned. Jackson had encouraged her to break the straitlaced bonds she'd grown up with, had been the only one to support her when she'd expressed a desire to get away for a while, see new places, try new things. She'd always believed him when he'd said it was only a matter of time until he broke away, himself. Had it just been talk? Was he really as deeply rooted here as so many others seemed to be?

As though sensing her questions, Jackson chuckled. "Don't look at me that way, Maddie. I haven't suddenly turned into Joe Average. Soon as I get enough money stashed away to support me in style for a while, I'm out of here. I was thinking of heading for Tahiti first. Maybe Bimini. You know, where the sun always shines and—"

"'—the women don't wear tops,'" Maddie quoted him. She'd heard him say it many times. Had she been naive to believe that his words had been anything more than idle fantasizing?

"You got it," he said cockily.

She was beginning to have second thoughts about her lack of discretion in unloading on Jackson. She didn't know what had suddenly gotten into her. "Jackson, what I said...about being stood up at the altar? Maybe we could just, um—"

"Consider it forgotten."

She smiled gratefully. "Thank you."

"Of course, you have to promise in return not to mention that I've been thoughtful and considerate. I have my wicked reputation to consider, you know."

She shook her head reprovingly. "A reputation you have very carefully cultivated. I still don't understand why you're so determined to convince everyone you're a selfish, shallow playboy, when there's really a nice guy lurking under that flashy exterior."

"Hey, quiet!" He made an exaggerated show of hastily looking around to make sure no one had overheard her words. "Someone might hear you. Truth is," he continued, turning back to her with a wry smile, "I really *am* basically selfish and shallow. On very rare occasions, I can overcome those natural tendencies when I make an effort to do so. But if I did it more often, everyone would start to expect it of me all the time, and it's just too much trouble on a regular basis."

Maddie laughed. "Honestly, Jackson. You're incorrigible."

"Isn't that what I just said?"

"You're also a very good friend."

He groaned and rubbed his forehead with one beringed hand. "Isn't that like saying a blind date had a nice personality? I've been trying to seduce you for months and all you can say is that I'm a good friend. I must be slipping."

"You? Impossible."

"Sounds promising. Does that mean you'll go home with me when we leave here?"

"No."

He sighed heavily. "Definitely slipping," he grumbled.

"Eat your ice cream, Jackson," she said, dipping a spoon into her own. "It's melting."

"If only my charm had the same effect on you."

Maddie laughed, and was grateful to him for the diversion.

JACKSON DROPPED Maddie off at her house at just after midnight. He walked her to the front door, brushed a kiss over her mouth and warned her to watch out for "lurking fiancés." And then he left, whistling beneath his teeth and acting as though he was amused by the entire evening.

Maddie shook her head, locked the front door behind her and tiptoed through the quiet, sleeping house to her upstairs bedroom.

Only then did she fall apart.

Her knees buckled, making her land on the bed with a soft thump. She hid her face in her hands.

What a day! How could she have known when it started that Case Brannigan would stroll back into her life, apparently intent on taking up where he'd left off six months ago?

At least now she had an explanation for his hasty departure from Cancún. But could she believe a word of it?

It sounded so daring and romantic—called away to rescue an old friend from terrible villains. A desperate, stealthy rescue that ended with the hero seriously wounded, in danger of never walking again. That same valiant hero struggling nobly to recuperate, making a vow to himself that he would not return to his bride an invalid.

It sounded, Maddie decided with a scowl, too daring and romantic to be real.

Obviously Case had been injured. Badly injured. His weight loss, the lines of pain carved into his face, the awkward limp—he couldn't have feigned those signs if he'd wanted to. But had it really happened the way he'd described? How did she know he was what he'd claimed to be?

When it came right down to it, Case Brannigan was a stranger to her. A stranger she'd almost married in a moment of weakness. And now he was back—but Maddie had changed. She wasn't sure whether she'd lost her courage, or found it, but she wasn't going to be such an easy mark for him this time. She wasn't taking everything he said on faith. She had no reason to believe his exotic tales, no basis for accepting his claim to want a normal, domestic future with her.

For all she knew, he was a con man. An adventurer. She'd heard about the type on "Geraldo" and "Donahue." Maybe he thought her half of the restaurant was worth more than it really was. Maybe he had some other scheme up his well-tailored sleeve. If so, he could forget it.

Maddie had fancied herself in love with Case on that beach in Cancún, even though he'd never actually said the words to her. During the past six months, she'd convinced herself that it hadn't been love. Merely infatuation. Maybe even a healthy case of lust.

Unfortunately, whatever it had been, she still felt it. She'd hadn't been able to change her feelings as easily as she'd changed her hair color, lost those extra pounds or traded her glasses for contact lenses.

Which didn't mean she *couldn't* change them. It was just going to take a bit more effort.

She had no intention of making a fool of herself again over the enigmatic Case Brannigan.

5

CASE SPENT most of the day Monday looking at houses for sale. He had two reasons for doing so. First, he had no intention of staying any longer than necessary in the Spartan little hotel room that was the best Mitchell's Fork had to offer. And second, it gave him something to do until he judged the time right to approach Maddie again.

He might not have been so patient with her had he not watched her with Babbit the night before. Had he suspected that Maddie's feelings for the guy were getting serious, Case might have been tempted to do something desperate. Like throwing her over his shoulder and whisking her to the nearest justice of the peace. But he'd watched them together at the fast-food restaurant, and then at her door when the date ended. He'd seen enough to convince him that Maddie and Babbit were not intimately involved. Not even close.

They'd never known he'd been watching them, of course. Case had lurked in enough shadows, secretly monitored too many clandestine meetings, to give away his presence to a couple of unsuspecting amateurs.

Maddie would probably be furious with him if she knew he'd followed her last night. But tough, he thought with a grim smile. As far as he was concerned, she'd given herself to him on that beach in Cancún—verbally, if not physically. And Case Brannigan protected what was his.

The real estate agent eyed Case's cold smile with visible trepidation. She was the jittery type, a meek little matron who sold houses for extra money, Case guessed. She'd probably never encountered anyone quite like him before.

He made an effort to give her a more natural smile. "This is more like what I had in mind," he said encouragingly, gesturing at the grounds surrounding them as they approached the third house she'd described to him. The other two had been all wrong, one too small, the other too boring. This place, however, had definite potential, Case decided as he moved toward the front door, the relieved-looking agent tagging nervously at his heels.

He supposed the style of the house was Country-Victorian. It nestled into a rolling lawn, with huge shade trees all around, and flower beds that would probably be beautiful later in the summer. A wrap-around porch decorated with gingerbread and turned-post railings led to double front doors with leaded-glass windows. He liked the little details on the outside. Pale yellow siding. Cream-painted trim. Fish-scale shingles in the gables. Cedar-shake roof. Lots of interesting angles and curves. Even an oval stained-glass window set over the front porch—probably in the upper section of an open foyer, he guessed.

Yeah, this one looked interesting. Much the way he'd envisioned a "real home" looked. "How many bedrooms?" he asked, noticing the house looked fairly big.

"Five," the agent squeaked. "The master suite is on the first floor, and the other four are upstairs. And there are four full baths and two half baths. The house is only ten years old, and the grounds cover seven acres. There's a little pond at the back of the property, and a nice back lawn that would be perfect for a swimming pool, should you decide to add one."

Case nodded. Five bedrooms sounded good. He wondered how many of them Maddie would be interested in filling with kids. A board squeaked underfoot as he climbed the stairs and crossed the wide porch. He paused to test it, and decided it was sound.

"There are probably a few maintenance chores to attend to," the agent said, sounding scrupulously honest. "It has been empty for almost a year now."

"How come?" Case asked, remembering to show at least minimal suspicion.

"It's—um, rather expensive for this area," she admitted. "It's larger and more expensively built than most homes around here. And, of course, heating and air-conditioning costs are higher because of the size."

Case relaxed. Money was not a problem. As for maintenance, that didn't bother him, either. All part of being a home owner, he'd heard. Of course, he'd never owned one, himself. He'd grown up in fleabag apartments, institutions and cheap-rent houses, and had spent the last fifteen years living out of a suitcase, for the most part. But he still remembered those childhood fantasies—a family, a dog, a nice home in which to entertain the friends he would have liked to have had.

"Big place," he said as he followed the agent into a two-story foyer that led to a sweeping, curved staircase. He could see into large, empty, curtainless rooms that opened off the foyer. A bookcase-lined library opened to his left, and a large, octagonal, window-walled room to his right. He hazarded a guess that it was a formal dining room. He mentally filled it with a big table and a gleaming chandelier. Of course, he pictured himself at the head of that table, Maddie at his right.

He'd never hosted a dinner party, he realized absently. He wondered if it was too late to learn how.

Maybe Maddie could teach him.

"It is a large house," the agent was saying, cutting into Case's daydream. "The people who built it came here from up north somewhere. They lived here until Mrs. Fielding wanted to go back to live near her grandchildren. They put the house on the market two years ago, but when it didn't sell, they moved, anyway, and left it in my agency's hands."

Case rubbed a hand along the polished walnut banister. "Hmm," he said, already half-sold. "Show me the rest."

A vaguely speculative gleam appeared in the agent's nervous eyes. She cleared her throat, squared her shoulders and went into a memorized spiel of the home's many features. The three-car garage. The detached woodshop—Case had always wanted to play with power tools. He smiled.

She showed him the two-story-tall family room with its massive fireplace. The master bedroom with another fireplace, French doors leading to yet another covered porch, and a bay-windowed sitting room. A kitchen filled with efficient-looking appliances and dark oak cabinetry. A cozy, octagonal morning room, just right for intimate family breakfasts. Upstairs were four nice-size bedrooms, and a lounge/game room with yet another fireplace.

"I like it," Case said.

The agent smiled, and suddenly she didn't look quite so wary. "I'm sure you'd be very happy here," she told him.

Case thought she might well be right. He hoped Maddie felt the same way.

"HE DID *WHAT*?" Telephone pressed to her ear, Maddie sank into the chair behind the cluttered desk in the restaurant office where she'd been doing weekly paperwork that afternoon.

"He made an offer on the Fielding place," her friend Jill answered cheerfully. "Sherry Holder showed it to him. She's so excited about the probable commission that she's already ordered a new car from McKenzie's Ford dealership."

Maddie could hardly believe it. "Why on earth would Case want a house that big?" she asked.

"It *is* big for a single guy. Five bedrooms, five or six bathrooms, a library and a den and an upstairs lounge, three fireplaces—there's even a butler's pantry!"

"I've never been inside it, of course, but I hear the rooms are large and open and the ceilings are all high. Sherry once told me that the house costs a fortune to heat and cool," Maddie mused out loud. She shook her head. "And I've also heard it has some maintenance problems that the Fieldings left unattended. Case couldn't possibly know what he's getting into."

"Sherry swore to me that she told him everything. She said he didn't even seem to hear the problems. He took one look at the place and said he wanted it."

Maddie groaned. This, she decided, was getting out of hand. How could she have predicted that Case would run out and buy a house the day after arriving in town? Not that she was particularly surprised by his choice of houses. The Fielding place was big, impressive, a bit overdone. Like Case's "courtship" of her.

The Fieldings had never really fit into Mitchell's Fork society, nor had they tried particularly hard, which was why Maddie had never been inside the house. Case was an outsider who'd been attracted to a house built by outsiders. It figured.

"I've been in the place. Sherry took me through once, a few months ago," Jill said. "It's a beautiful house, really, but the color scheme is terrible. Too many pastels to really suit all the dark-stained wood trim. Being a man, Case probably didn't even notice." A hint of laughter entered her voice. "You know how I love decorating. I'll be happy to help you pick new paints and carpets and wallpapers when you move in."

"When I— Jill, I am *not* moving into the Fielding place!"

"Mmm. Tell that to your fiancé," Jill teased. "Sherry said he must have mentioned you about fifty times during the three hours she spent with him."

Maddie groaned. "I suppose she's telling everyone that."

"Most likely. I can't wait to meet this guy."

"Fine. I'll introduce you. Maybe he'll decide you'll make a more suitable little wife for him."

Jill laughed. "From everything I've heard about him, I'm beginning to wish he would. Lisa and Anita are telling everyone he's very nice—in a deliciously dangerous sort of way. Lisa says Jeff is already nuts about him, and is even hinting that if you don't want him, he wouldn't mind his mom making a play for the guy. Sherry said he scared her half to death, but she couldn't help noticing that he was about the sexiest male to ever appear in these parts. Jackson's calling him the Terminator. He claims he was taking his life in his hands by going with you to the movie last night. Of course, he was laughing his fool head off the whole time he was saying all that. It was obvious he thinks the whole situation is hysterical."

Maddie sighed heavily. She wasn't surprised that Jill had heard all the gossip. Jill worked as a teller in the only bank in Mitchell's Fork. Very little in the way of local news escaped her. "What am I going to do, Jill?"

"There's only one thing for you to do," her friend intoned solemnly.

"What?"

"Order a wedding gown. And you'd better ask me to be maid of honor, or I'm going to be royally—"

"Damn it, Jill, you're as bad as Jackson! This is serious. The guy really thinks I'm going to marry him. He's buying that house with the intention of living there with me!"

"According to your aunt and cousin, he has good reason to feel that way," Jill said a bit more seriously. "They said he implied that you would already be married if he hadn't been called away from Cancún on business. Is that true, Maddie?"

Maddie could almost picture herself entering Señor Ruiz's little office, wearing her white eyelet sundress, trembling but determined. And, though she cringed to admit it now, she knew that if Case had been waiting for her then, she would have married him. Just like that.

"Maddie?" Jill prodded after a moment.

Maddie swallowed. "Yes. I guess it is true. But—"

"I can't believe you never said anything about it to me when you got home." Jill spoke quietly, with attempted nonchalance, but Maddie heard a touch of hurt in her friend's voice. Very similar to the pain she'd heard in her father's voice the evening before.

She hadn't meant to hurt them. She'd been tempted on more than one occasion to confide in them, and tell them what she'd been going through for the past six months. But she just hadn't been able to talk about this. She hadn't been able to explain how Case had made her feel, how he'd smiled at her and taken her hand and she'd tumbled into love with him, even though he was a stranger to her. And she couldn't admit to them how humiliated she had been when she'd realized how gullible, how vulnerable she must have seemed to him.

"I'm sorry, Jill. I just . . . couldn't."

"Yeah, sure. I understand." But it was obvious that she didn't, not entirely. "I'd better let you get back to work. We'll talk later, okay?"

"Of course."

"Oh, and Maddie?"

"Yes?"

"I know I've been teasing you a lot about this, but if you really need to talk . . . I'm here, okay?"

Maddie's eyes felt suddenly damp. "I know, Jill. And thanks. I might just take you up on that."

"Anytime, kid. Bye." She hung up before Maddie could reply.

Maddie buried her face in her hands and groaned loudly.

Why had she ever filled out that stupid sweepstakes entry form at the supermarket? How could she have known that she would be changing her entire life by doing so?

CASE PUT the windows of the Ferrari down that evening to allow him to enjoy the fragrant, warm, spring air. It was just after 6:00 p.m., and he was hungry. He figured it was time to sample the menu at Mike and Maddie's place.

One arm propped comfortably on the open window frame, he braked for a red light, humming beneath his breath with the song playing on the radio. He felt good. He hoped Maddie was in a more approachable mood this evening.

A shiny, chrome-and-lights-bedecked pickup truck pulled up beside him in the left-turn lane. Heavy metal music blasted from the open windows of the pickup, drowning the oldies station Case had tuned in to. Three teenage boys were crowded into the seat of the truck, one in an oversize Western hat, the other two in baseball caps. All of them were studying the Ferrari.

The truck's driver revved the engine, making Case suspect the vehicle had been modified for speed and power. He glanced sideways, noted the punks looked as if they were itching for trouble and decided to ignore them. He looked at the traffic light, willing it to change to green.

"Hey," the boy sitting closest to Case called out. "How fast does that thing go?"

Case debated answering for a moment, then sighed lightly and said, "It goes the speed limit."

The boys snickered, and made jeering remarks. The truck engine revved again, remaining in place even though the turn arrow had lighted. "C'mon, Grandpa. Let's see what that pansy little Eye-talian skateboard can do," the driver yelled.

Case thought he caught the smell of beer through the open windows. He slanted his most intimidating look at the troublemakers. "Better hurry home, boys. Your mamas are calling you."

He probably shouldn't have provoked them that way, but being called grandpa had smarted his pride. Hell, he was only thirty-five. He could easily beat the living daylights out of any one of these runny-nosed punks—all three at once, for that matter. And then he reminded himself that he wanted to fit in here. Beating up the local progeny was probably not the best way to ingratiate himself with the townspeople.

His light changed to green before the boys could recover enough to retaliate. Case pressed the accelerator, and left them behind in a blur of finely tuned Italian engine power. He checked the rearview mirror to make sure they weren't following, and was relieved to see that they were nowhere in sight.

Maybe they'd been all talk, he thought, relaxing again. Just having a little fun. In the future, he would try harder to remember that he was a civilian now, that there were no longer enemies lurking behind every bush.

The first thing Case noticed when he pulled into the parking lot of the restaurant was that it was empty. Completely. Frowning, he pulled up to the front and read the hours posted on the entrance door.

Well, hell. The restaurant closed after lunch on Sundays and didn't reopen until 11:00 a.m. on Tuesdays. So where was a hungry guy supposed to eat on Monday evening?

It occurred to him that maybe Maddie hadn't eaten yet, either. Maybe it wasn't too late to convince her to dine with him.

He turned the car around and headed toward her home.

"I'VE BEEN WONDERING when you were going to show up," the housekeeper drawled when he opened the door to Case.

Uncertain how to take Frank's words, Case cleared his throat. "Is Maddie in?"

"Yeah. She's in the backyard, feeding the dogs."

Case took a step backward. "I'll just go around and look for her, then."

"You staying for dinner again?"

"I thought I'd ask Maddie to have dinner out with me."

Frank shrugged. "Just let me know how many places to set at the table." With that, he closed the door.

Case shook his head and followed the sidewalk around the side of the house in search of Maddie. He thought again that she certainly lived in an odd household—or at least, he considered the people who lived here odd. Of course, they probably felt the same way about him.

He found Maddie pouring dry dog food into two large aluminum bowls while the dogs danced impatiently nearby. "All right, guys, wait a minute, will you?" she grumbled, pushing one mutt out of the way when he almost knocked her over trying to get to his dinner. "Jeez, you'd think you hadn't eaten in weeks."

She looked great, Case decided, standing quietly behind her, unobserved. She was wearing snug jeans, a close-fitting pink T-shirt and white leather sneakers. Her softly gleaming hair swung free around her face. He was finally getting used to her new image—in fact, as attracted as he'd been to her before, he found her even more desirable now. Something told him he would have felt the same way even if she hadn't changed at all.

Glasses or contacts, mousy brown or sexy gold-streaked hair—it made no difference to him. He wanted Maddie, and the months he'd spent away from her had only increased that hunger.

The dogs attacked their bowls, wolfing down the kibble with loud crunches and appreciative wriggles. Maddie watched them for a moment, chuckling, then turned and spotted Case. The large plastic pitcher that had held the dog food hit the ground with a thud.

"Oh," she said, her cheeks flaming. "You startled me."

"Sorry."

She bent to retrieve the pitcher. She seemed to have regained her composure by the time she straightened again. "What are you doing here?"

"I came to ask you to dinner."

"You could have called."

"I'm sorry," he repeated. "I thought you'd be working tonight. I stopped by the restaurant and found out it's closed on Mondays."

She nodded, twisting the pitcher between her hands.

"So, how about it?" he prodded. "Dinner?"

"I'm really not dressed to go out."

"You look fine." He motioned toward his own khaki slacks and cotton sport shirt. "We'll go someplace casual."

"I was planning to do some paperwork tonight."

"We'll make it an early evening, then," he said promptly, torn between amusement and exasperation at her obvious stalling. "It's only dinner, Maddie."

She sighed. "All right, I'll go. I want to talk to you, anyway," she added rather ominously.

Case could have wished for a bit more enthusiasm on her part, but he decided not to press his luck. "Whatever you say, Maddie."

She rolled her eyes. "Yeah, right," she muttered. "I just wish it was that easy."

Before he could comment, she stepped around him. "I'll go in and wash up. I'll meet you out front in ten minutes."

"You're not asking me in?"

"And give you a chance to start planning a wedding with my family? I think not."

He laughed. "You don't trust me an inch, do you, sweetheart?"

To his secret delight, she blushed again in response to the endearment, though she scowled ferociously at him. "Not an inch," she assured him flatly.

It was all he could do not to kiss her silly right there on the spot. He shoved his hands into his pockets. "Out front. Ten minutes," he said.

She nodded curtly. And then she turned and stalked into the house.

You're mine, Maddie Carmichael, Case thought, watching her retreat to the house. *What's it going to take for me to convince you?*

Whatever it was, he would do it. Case Brannigan never accepted failure when he set his sites on an objective. And he'd never wanted anything more than Maddie Carmichael as his wife.

6

"THIS IS the first time I've really been alone with you since I arrived in Mitchell's Fork," Case said with great satisfaction a half hour later.

From across the booth, Maddie raised an eyebrow and glanced around the moderately crowded pizza parlor. "I wouldn't exactly call this being alone."

He shrugged. "You know what I mean."

A plump waitress approached the table, order pad in hand. "Hey, Maddie," she said by way of greeting. "This the guy everyone's been talking about?"

Maddie made a face. "Probably. JoNell, this is Case Brannigan. Case, JoNell Cushing. She and I went to junior high together."

"Nice to meet you," Case said, wondering if the rather dour-looking woman ever smiled.

"Same here. Y'all ready to order?"

Maddie seemed relieved that JoNell wasn't inclined to stay and visit. "I'll have the salad bar and a diet cola," she said briskly.

Case frowned. "You don't like pizza?"

"Of course. But it's terribly fattening . . ."

Case waved off the rest of her excuse. "Bring us a large pizza. With everything," he added. "And I'll have a beer."

JoNell shook her head. "This is a dry county, mister."

"Oh. Well, a cola, then."

"You got it." JoNell stuck the pencil behind her ear and ambled away.

Case turned back to Maddie, only to find her tapping the laminated tabletop with one finger, a scowl creasing her forehead. "Why did you do that?" she demanded.

"Do what?"

"You know what. You ordered pizza, even though I'd just said I wanted the salad bar."

"Did you look at the salad bar on the way in? There's nothing on it but lettuce and a few limp-looking vegetables."

"Still, it was what I wanted—and you had no right to cancel my order. The only reason I didn't say anything in front of JoNell is that I didn't want to add to all the gossip going around about us."

"JoNell didn't look like a gossiper to me," Case remarked, considering the woman's brusque, no-nonsense manner.

"Then maybe you should look again. She wallows in it. Just like most everyone else around here. There's little else to do for entertainment."

Relieved that she'd gotten distracted from his unintentional arrogance in ordering the pizza, Case pursued the subject. "When we met in Cancún, you told me you loved your hometown. Why are you suddenly so critical of it?"

"I do love my hometown," she answered defensively. "It's just...well, I've started to realize that there's so much more to experience out there. So many things I've never done. And I think it's past time I find out what they are."

Case shook his head. "We're back to that, are we?"

"Yes. Nothing has changed."

He was torn between shaking her and hugging her. He realized now that he must have hurt her badly in Cancún, and he didn't blame her for being a bit wary of him now. But couldn't she see what a mistake she would be making if she set out on her own, unprepared for what she might find during those romantic adventures about which she fantasized? Case knew what was out there, all too well. Maddie didn't have a clue.

He tried to speak calmly, reasonably. "I understand your desire to see more of the world. That's perfectly natural. A lot of people enjoy traveling—in pairs or in supervised tour groups. But traveling alone is dangerous and reckless. Almost an invitation for disaster, especially if you're serious about going into those back villages."

"You mean, like the disastrous mistake I almost made the last time I traveled alone?" she asked a bit too sweetly. "Well, you can stop worrying about me, Case. I don't make the same mistake twice."

He held on to his patience with an effort. "What I'm trying to say," he said from between clenched teeth, "is that you can still have your adventures after we're married. We'll go to Europe for our honeymoon, if you like. I can show you places you wouldn't find on any package tour. I'll take you to those damned out-of-the-way villages and isolated locations—and I'll keep you safe there. Australia, Asia, the Caribbean—just say where you want to go and I'll take you."

Her eyes had widened. "You've been to all those places?"

"Most of them."

"And you can afford to travel there now?"

He shrugged. "I have money. I haven't spent much of my earnings for the past few years—other than my car, I have simple tastes. And I've been told I have a shrewd head for investments."

"Like the Fielding place? Is that an investment?"

He winced. "You've heard about that already?"

"Sherry's already spending her commission. That place costs a fortune, Case."

"As I said, my investments are doing very well, bringing in a more than comfortable income," he said a bit stiffly. He didn't want to believe that Maddie's feelings toward him would be influenced by finances—but he thought she had a right to know he could support her. As traditional husbands were supposed to do, he reminded himself.

"I have enough to buy and maintain the house, with enough left over to allow some travel. I thought I'd concentrate on investments full-time once we get settled in. Maybe set up a small financial-consulting practice. Surely some of the farmers and small-business owners in this area could use some financial-management advice."

Maddie suddenly shook her head. "I'm sorry. Your finances are none of my business. I was just... surprised. I didn't realize the government paid so well."

"For certain assignments, they do. And, as I said, I've a head for investments."

"Good for you. Then you shouldn't have any trouble at all finding a wife," she said brusquely.

Case wondered if she was deliberately trying to make him angry. "I have no intention of buying a wife."

"If you're counting on your charm to win you a wife, you might want to reconsider," she suggested airily. "Not many modern women go for the arrogant, bossy, take-charge type."

"You didn't seem to have any complaints about my charm—or lack of it—in Cancún," Case retorted, thinking pensively of those long, passionate kisses in the moonlight.

The memories must have been reflected in his eyes. Maddie blushed. "I repeat," she muttered. "I don't make the same mistake twice."

JoNell plopped a pizza onto the table between them, oblivious to the tension that was so thick Case felt as though he could slice it with a pizza cutter. "Need anything else?" the waitress asked.

Case and Maddie both shook their heads.

"Enjoy your meal," the gruff waitress said perfunctorily as she moved away.

Case cleared his throat. "Look, Maddie, I know I've handled everything wrong since I came to town. I'm very sorry I hurt you in Cancún, and I'm sorry I've caused you discomfort in front of your family and friends here. To be honest, I thought everything had been settled in Cancún. I thought you'd be waiting for me, ready to take up where we left off. I suppose that *was* rather arrogant on my part—"

"Yes, it most certainly was."

He nodded. "All right. I'm sorry for that, too. But can't we put the anger and hurt feelings aside—at least for tonight? We were great together in Cancún, you have to admit that."

What might have been a sad, wistful expression flitted through her eyes, so quickly he almost missed it. Her voice was a bit gruff when she spoke. "We had fun," she agreed. "But it wasn't real, Case. It was nothing more than a vacation romance that almost got out of hand."

He wanted so badly to heatedly dispute her casual dismissal of what they'd shared. It hurt, he discovered, to have her speak about it that way. He managed to speak calmly. "I don't agree. I think it was very real. I know it was for me."

She looked away, so that he couldn't tell what she was thinking by her expression.

When she remained silent, Case spoke again. "All right. We'll agree to put Cancún behind us—for now. We'll start over, if you like. I want a chance to prove to you that what we found before is still there, that it can be just as good between us in Mitchell's Fork, Mississippi—or anywhere else."

She looked at him suspiciously. "What are you suggesting?"

"Dating. Going out, getting to know each other again. I know you're busy at the restaurant, and I don't expect you to neglect your job or your other obligations, but I'm sure there will be time for us to be together. Apparently, you have found time to date in the past few months," he couldn't resist adding stiffly.

The corners of her mouth twitched, but she didn't quite smile. "I don't know, Case—"

"I won't push you," he promised, tempted to cross his fingers beneath the table. At least he would try not to push, he silently vowed. "I only want to see you. Will you give me that chance?"

"You aren't going to forbid me to see anyone else, are you?" she asked, her question holding an underlying challenge.

He phrased his answer very carefully. "I won't pretend I'll like it if you date anyone else—but I certainly have no right to forbid you to do so." *Yet,* he added mentally.

She nodded emphatically. "Exactly."

"So?" Case prodded, impatience barely reined.

She reached for a slice of pizza. "I'm out with you now, aren't I?"

"Does that mean you'll go out with me again?"

She smiled. "I guess we'll just have to see how tonight goes first. Isn't that the way dating usually works? One outing at a time?"

He supposed he'd have to be content with that. As she'd said, she was with him tonight. He intended to make the most of it. He lifted a thickly topped pizza slice onto his own plate. "This looks good," he said. "I can't remember the last time I had pizza."

She seemed relieved that he'd changed the subject.

MADDIE *WAS* RELIEVED that Case had changed the topic from their complicated relationship to more innocuous subjects. For the next half hour, they talked about Mitchell's Fork. It seemed that Case was almost insatiably curious about the town he'd impulsively decided to make his home. He asked questions about the history of the area, the prevailing industries, the median income, the social climate, the politics.

She struggled gamely to answer his questions candidly, explaining that, like most small towns, Mitchell's Fork had both its charms and its drawbacks. The people were friendly and warm, but blatantly nosy, she said—as if he hadn't already noticed. The area was beautiful, natural and unspoiled, but poor. The politics were also typical of small towns, operating primarily on the nepotistic good-old-boy system.

"Your Aunt Nettie seemed disgusted with that system," Case commented.

Maddie nodded. "Most people are. They just won't take the necessary steps to make changes."

"For example?"

"Well, every four years for the past two decades, they've elected the same man for mayor—Bobby Sloane. The guy's a joke. A smarmy ex-used-car salesman who wouldn't know the truth if it slapped his jaws, as Aunt Nettie would say. He's owned body and soul by Major Cooper, the plant owner you heard about yesterday. Everyone despises Sloane, but they're all afraid to vote against him. He's coming up for reelection in November, and although I'll vote against him, I can almost guarantee you he'll win again."

Case frowned and shook his head. "That's crazy."

"That's politics," she reminded him. "Look at the situation in D.C.—the incumbents who've been in office for years and years, no matter how many scandals or indiscretions they've been exposed in. It's the same here. As for our sheriff—Buck McAdams—well, he's an even bigger joke. Every stereotype you've ever seen or read of the incompetent lawman was probably based on McAdams."

Case was frowning even more deeply now, and Maddie realized this wasn't exactly what he wanted to hear about her town. What had he expected, she wondered in exasperation? Mayberry? He most definitely had an idealistic view of "normal life," as he put it. How long would it be before he ran back to the excitement of his former life-style?

"What about the local press?" he asked. "Doesn't the town newspaper make any effort to expose these guys for what they are?"

"The *Mitchell's Fork Weekly News?*" Maddie asked wryly. "Have you seen it yet?"

"Well, no . . ."

"The hottest news you'll find in that little paper is that Mrs. Underwood's sister from Cleveland visited her last week and was welcomed with a tea at the Ladies' Charity Club. There will probably be a whole page of photos to accompany that story—you know, Mrs. Carson in the new linen suit that she drove all the way to Memphis to buy, Mrs. Bakerman serving her famous strawberry shortcake, Mrs. Nowlin with her granddaughter, Heather, last year's Junior Miss Mitchell's Fork—"

Case held up a hand. "I get the idea."

"Still think you want to settle down here?"

"Sure. But don't you think it's time a few local citizens got involved in making some changes? If everyone hates the system, as you said, then surely—"

Maddie stopped him by shaking her head. "You just don't get it, Case. If you want to be accepted, you'll stay out of it. No matter how much the locals may complain about the system, they're not going to take kindly to an outsider who comes in and starts advocating change. The Fieldings—the 'Yankees' who built the house you're looking at—tried that at first. Trust me, it didn't endear them to Mitchell's Fork."

"But—"

"Well, well. If it ain't Mr. Speed Limit."

The insolent drawl broke into their conversation and caused both Maddie and Case to turn curiously toward its source. Maddie cringed to see Danny Cooper and two of his obnoxious friends standing near their table, eyeing Case in obvious challenge.

Seventeen-year-old Danny was a startlingly handsome young man—almost too pretty, Maddie had always thought. His finest feature were his eyes, which were a clear, intense blue fringed in long, curling lashes. Though she'd heard others wax poetic about those eyes, Maddie had never been quite comfortable on the few occasions when she was the focus of the boy's attention. There was a streak of meanness in Danny that Maddie could almost see lurking in the crystalline depths.

She knew the two kids with Danny, as well. Dark-haired, dark-eyed Kale Sloane—the mayor's son—and Steve Langford, a lanky, disjointed boy with a bad complexion and a perpetual sneer. These were the three who had beaten up Jeff. How had Case gotten involved with them already?

Case glanced at the boys, then turned to Maddie. "Have another slice of pizza," he urged her. "There's plenty left."

It was obvious that he had no intention of acknowledging the teenagers.

Apparently, Danny wasn't discouraged. "Hear you've been telling folks you're some sort of spy or something," he said to Case, his tone making his disbelief clear. "Driving that fancy car, pretending you're going to buy the Fielding place—what kind of scam you running here, mister?"

"My dad says he don't believe you're a spy," Steve piped in. "He says you're up to no good."

"My dad's mayor of this town," Kale said, not to be left out. "He don't hold with liars and con men."

Maddie snorted.

Kale looked at her suspiciously, but she resisted the impulse to tell him exactly what she thought of his father. He was just a kid, she reminded herself. An obnoxious one, but a kid, nonetheless.

Case was still ignoring the boys, but his face had gone so hard and cold that Maddie wondered if the kids were stupid not to recognize a potentially dangerous man when they saw one. She assumed their courage was a combination of bravado and beer.

"Danny Cooper, if you and your friends ain't going to order, then you best be running along," JoNell called out aggressively, hands on her ample hips. "We don't want no trouble out of you boys tonight."

"We'll leave when we're ready," Kale retorted, tilting his cowboy hat farther back on his head.

Case's eyes narrowed. Maddie reached out quickly to cover his hand with hers, sensing that he was close to the edge. "JoNell can handle them," she assured him.

Sure enough, JoNell was bearing down on the boys like an angry mother bear.

"Shoot, I'm bored with this place, anyway," Danny drawled, edging toward the exit. "Only a bunch of old wimps hanging around in here tonight."

"Out," JoNell repeated, pointing a stern finger toward the door.

The boys left, though at a leisurely pace that implied they were leaving only because they wanted to, not because they'd been told to.

"Sorry about that, Maddie," JoNell said, including Case in the apology by nodding to him. "Someone oughtta introduce those boys to Mr. Kennedy's 'board of education,' if you know what I mean."

"Mr. Kennedy was a teacher JoNell and I had in junior high," Maddie explained after the waitress moved away. "He had a big wooden paddle that he called the board of education. That was before corporal punishment was banned in public schools, of course."

"I'm not so sure it should have been," Case muttered, looking out the window beside him at the fancy pickup truck that was just leaving the parking lot with a defiant squeal of tires.

"I don't approve of using violence against children," Maddie said primly. And then she smiled. "But in Danny's case, I could make an exception...."

Case chuckled. "Yeah. Me, too. If you hadn't stopped me, I just might have made that exception right here."

Suddenly aware that she was still holding his hand, Maddie flushed and removed it, annoyed to find that her fingers seemed to be tingling from the contact. She laced her fingers in her lap. "I was just making sure you didn't do anything foolish," she said firmly. "You're an adult and they're a bunch of wild kids. Nothing good could come of a confrontation between you."

Case muttered something unintelligible, but let the subject drop. Maddie released a long breath and turned her attention back to her dinner, feeling as though a potential crisis had just been narrowly averted.

Case Brannigan was definitely out of his element in Mitchell's Fork, she thought with a touch of melancholy. Surely it wouldn't be long before he realized it, too.

CASE MADE a slight detour on his way to Maddie's house after dinner. Though curious, Maddie didn't ask where he was going, since he looked as though he had a specific destination in mind.

She looked at him with a lifted eyebrow when he turned onto a gravel road leading to a favorite local fishing lake. Bordered on either side by dense woods, the rutted road curved and twisted, ending in a concrete boat ramp at the water's edge. Case pulled over to the side of the road, turned off the headlights and killed the engine.

It was dark in the car, the only illumination coming through the windows from the full moon above them. They were the only humans around at the moment; the only sounds outside the vehicle came from frogs, crickets, owls and other nocturnal wildlife.

"I found this place when I was driving around exploring this afternoon," Case said. "There were a couple of older men sitting on the banks fishing, and a man and a woman in an aluminum boat out in the middle of the lake. They all looked so relaxed, I couldn't help envying them."

"Fishing is a favorite pastime around here," Maddie agreed, trying to pretend it didn't bother her to be alone with him like this. The interior of his sports car suddenly seemed very small, very intimate. She tried not to notice. "My father and I have fished here many times. The lake is stocked with bream and bass and crappie. We have a family fish fry at our place every fall."

"Sounds like fun."

"Yes. Do you like to fish?"

"It's been years since I've tried. I'll be lucky to remember how to bait a hook."

"I'm sure it will come back to you."

"Yeah. Probably." He looked at the moon-swept water thoughtfully. "Maybe I should buy a boat."

Maddie shifted in her seat. "Maybe you should hang around a while longer before you invest in expensive fishing equipment," she suggested. "You might just find out that you hate it here."

"I don't think so."

"It's not the Norman Rockwell town you've imagined, Case. I thought you'd already figured that out by now."

He shrugged. "So the town has its flaws. So do I. If the local folk can get used to me, I can get used to them."

Maddie shook her head in exasperation at his sheer stubbornness. "I don't understand you," she admitted.

He turned to her. "I know," he said gently. "But you will."

"Oh, Case. What am I going to do with you?"

She'd meant the question rhetorically. She should have known he would take it literally.

"Marry me," he said.

She sighed.

He laughed softly. "Will you at least kiss me?"

It was a good thing Maddie was still strapped in her seat, because her knees went weak at the liquid seduction in his husky voice. How many times had she heard just that tone in her dreams of Cancún? How many times had she reached out for him in her sleep, only to be devastated to find herself alone again?

"Case—"

"Only a kiss, Maddie," he murmured, inching toward her. "That's not too much to ask on a date, is it?"

With him, it could well be too much to ask. She wasn't at all sure she would be content just to kiss him. Not that she wanted to admit that, of course. She lifted her chin. "Only a kiss," she repeated.

"Of course." He gave her a suspiciously piratical smile, his teeth very white in the darkness, and deftly unfastened her seat belt. Before she could change her mind, he drew her into his arms.

Case took his time before kissing her. First, he brushed a strand of hair away from her cheek. Then he ran his thumb across her lower lip, very slowly. He shifted closer, so close his breath warmed her skin, his mouth hovering so near hers she could almost taste him. Almost.

It was Maddie who closed that small space between them. Unable to wait any longer, she pressed her mouth to his.

Even then, Case held back. The kiss was slow, gentle. Chaste. Very much a tentative, first-date kiss. And it made Maddie want to scream in frustration.

She knew exactly how deliciously Case could kiss when he made an effort.

Maybe the old Maddie would have been content with this sweet, utterly safe kiss. The new one was more bold, more daring. She closed her arms around his neck and slipped her tongue between his slightly parted lips.

As though he'd been waiting for that subtle invitation, Case suddenly crushed her mouth beneath his, his arms closing around her so tightly she could hardly breathe—which didn't matter, because she'd suddenly forgotten how.

He kissed her deeply, hungrily. Kissed her so heatedly, she melted against him, aching for more.

His hand swept her back, lingering at the curve of her waist, the gentle flare of her hip. He stroked her thigh, and she could feel the heat of his touch even through the washed-soft denim of her jeans. She shivered, imagining how his work-roughened palms would feel on her bare skin.

Case allowed her to draw a breath, but kissed her again before she could clear her mind. He cupped her face in his left hand for a moment, tilting her mouth to a new angle, and then he moved the hand downward, stroking her throat, her shoulder. Her breasts.

She shuddered, feeling the response course through her. And then she strained closer to him, ignoring the gearshift that was poking uncomfortably into her abdomen.

Somehow he found his way beneath the hem of her T-shirt. His palm was hot against her stomach, as deliciously rough as she'd imagined. Slowly—oh, so slowly—he slid his hand upward.

Her bra was little more than a frivolous swath of lace. He found the front clasp and released it with a skill she would frown about later. When she could think again.

His thumb circled her hardened nipple, making Maddie gasp into his mouth.

"Maddie." His voice was hoarse, his lips moving against hers. "If you knew how badly I've wanted to touch you like this. How many nights I've lain awake, wanting you."

She laid a hand on his chest, and felt his heart pounding beneath her palm. Pounding as heavily, as feverishly as her own. Weakened by the evidence that he was as deeply affected by their kisses as she, she lifted her mouth to his again.

This time, Case kissed her so thoroughly, so hungrily that she thought she'd go up in flames, right there in the passenger seat of his car. Her breath caught in her throat, and her pulse raced so rapidly she grew dizzy with reaction.

She wanted him. She'd wanted him in Cancún, and she hadn't stopped wanting him since. She'd never wanted any other man this badly. This desperately.

It was fear, more than prudence, that finally brought Maddie to her senses. What was she doing? She'd promised herself she wouldn't let Case do this to her again. Made a vow that she wouldn't be swayed by his practiced kisses and seductive caresses. And yet, here she was, plastered all over him again, ready to do almost anything he asked of her. And all she'd agreed to was a kiss.

She tore herself out of his arms. "It's time for you to take me home now, Case," she said in a voice she hardly recognized as her own.

She thought for a moment that he was going to argue. She saw the denial flash across his face. And then he drew a deep, unsteady breath, cleared his throat and nodded. "All right," he said. "If that's what you want."

Relieved, she tucked her T-shirt back into the waistband of her jeans and fastened her seat belt, scooting as far away from him as possible within the confines of the car. Case sent her a chiding look, but didn't say anything as he started the engine.

LIGHTS STILL BLAZED in the windows of the Carmichael farmhouse. Case walked Maddie to the door, but didn't ask to be invited inside. "Will you see me tomorrow?" he asked.

"I have to work tomorrow."

He frowned, but nodded. "All right. Later in the week, then."

Maddie drew a deep breath. "I'm not sure that's such a good idea."

His frown deepened. "It's just a date, Maddie."

She made a face. "Right. Like it was 'just a kiss' at the lake," she muttered.

"I stopped when you asked," he reminded her. "I've promised you I won't ask for anything more than you want to give."

He was going to break her heart again, she thought in despair. She knew it, and there didn't seem to be anything she could do to stop it. "Call me later in the week," she said wearily, hoping she'd recover her willpower in the meantime.

He nodded. "All right. Good night, Maddie."

"Good night, Case."

He moved toward her, but she slipped into the house before he could kiss her once more. She practically closed the door in his face.

She simply couldn't handle another kiss right now. Not while she was still a trembling mass of jelly from the last one.

She heard Case hesitate outside the door, as though tempted to barge in after her. And then she heard his footsteps crossing the porch and going down the steps to the sidewalk. Moments later, his car started with a muted roar of the powerful engine, which quickly faded to silence.

Maddie sagged against the door, resting her forehead against the unyielding wooden surface for a long moment. Sounds finally penetrated her foggy mind—the television, voices in the den, water running in the kitchen.

She straightened and ran a shaky hand through her hair, restoring it to some semblance of order. And then she pasted on a bright, utterly fake smile and went to join her family.

7

LUNCHTIME BUSINESS at Mike and Maddie's seemed better than usual on Tuesday. It didn't take long for Maddie to figure out why. Everyone wanted to know about the mysterious man who'd brought a buzz of excitement to Mitchell's Fork.

"Is it true he's a government spy?" one woman wanted to know.

"No, he wasn't a spy. He was in law enforcement. DEA," Maddie explained.

"I heard he's buying the Fielding place to open a bed and breakfast. They say he's going to build some sort of tourist attraction here," a longtime resident said disapprovingly.

"He isn't opening a bed and breakfast," Maddie replied with strained patience. "If he buys the Fielding place, it will be as a private home."

"Kind of big for a single man, don't you think?"

Maddie was annoyed with herself for flushing. "That's really none of our business, is it?"

"I heard he and Jackson Babbit got into a fistfight over you," the town barber, and most avid gossip, whispered to Maddie. "Right in front of your whole family."

"That's ridiculous. And totally untrue," Maddie snapped, rapidly losing all tolerance for the townsfolk's curiosity. "Now, Hank, are you going to order lunch, or not? I have other customers waiting."

Hank ordered the daily special in a disgruntled mumble. Maddie knew he was more annoyed that she hadn't given him any juicy details than he was offended by her curtness.

Maddie was relieved when Jill was the next customer to enter. "It's been horrible," she murmured as she led her tiny, dark-haired friend to a corner table. "You wouldn't believe the rumors!"

"Of course I would," Jill answered cheerfully. "I started most of them."

Groaning, Maddie motioned Jill into a chair. "This is no time for your sick sense of humor," she chided. "I'm dying, here."

Jill chuckled. "Sorry. I couldn't resist. But I do know the rumors. I heard them all at the bank this morning."

Maddie shook her head in disgust. "It just makes me crazy. You would think the people in this town would have better things to do than sit around gossiping about my personal life—or about Case's, for that matter."

"C'mon, Maddie, Mitchell's Fork isn't the only town obsessed with gossip. Why do you think those supermarket tabloids sell so well, even though everyone knows that what they report is a bunch of bologna? If a mysterious stranger comes to town, people are going to want to know more about him. They're curious. It's only human."

"It's annoying."

"So, whoever said humans weren't annoying?"

"I guess you have a point," Maddie admitted with a reluctant smile. "What will you have for lunch?"

Jill had just finished placing her order, when she noticed the man standing in the doorway to the dining room. "Wow," she murmured. "Let me guess—that's Case."

Maddie whipped her head around. And then gulped. "Yes," she sighed. "That's Case."

"Oh, heavens. Are you *sure* you don't want him, Maddie? 'Cause if you don't, I am most definitely available."

There was no mistaking the lust in Jill's voice as she eyed Case's hard, lean body. Maddie glared at her friend. "You don't even know him."

"What's left to know?" Jill asked with a shrug. "He's gorgeous. He apparently has money. He's planning on settling down in a beautiful house and starting a family. Unless he has a kinky thing about wearing women's underwear, I can't see a problem. Come to think of it, that would be okay, too, as long as he buys his own and leaves mine alone."

Maddie made a sound of disgust. "You really *do* have a warped sense of humor, don't you? And keep your voice down, for Pete's sake. Next thing you know, there'll be a rumor going around about Case being a cross-dresser or some such non—"

"Looks like I got here just in time," Case said from directly behind Maddie's shoulder. "What the hell are you talking about, Maddie?"

Maddie blushed crimson. Jill only laughed.

All too aware that they were the center of attention in the crowded dining room, Maddie swallowed a groan. "Case," she said resignedly. "This is my former best friend, Jill Parsons. Jill, Case Brannigan."

"I can't tell you how nice it is to meet you," Jill crooned, extending a hand to Case and ignoring Maddie's description of her.

Case held Jill's hand a bit longer than Maddie deemed strictly necessary. "It's nice to meet you, too."

"Are you here for lunch?"

"Yes."

"Dining alone?"

"Yes."

Jill smiled. "So am I. Won't you join me?"

Maddie opened her mouth in instinctive protest. Before she could speak, someone called out from a nearby table, "Hey, Maddie. We're ready to order here."

"Thank you," Case said to Jill, already moving toward the empty chair at her table. "I would be delighted to join you."

Maddie tried again. "But—"

"Maddie," her father said, passing quickly as he attempted to make up for her inattention to their customers. "Table four's getting impatient."

"Don't let me keep you from your work, Maddie," Case urged with a wicked smile. "Just bring me whatever Jill's having."

Since her name was now being called from more than one direction, Maddie couldn't linger any longer. She threw one last seething glance over her shoulder as she moved away. Heaven only knew what Jill would say to Case, or vice versa, she fumed. It wasn't that she was jealous—of *course* she wasn't jealous, why should she be? It was only that she didn't trust either one of them an inch, even though Jill was truly her best friend and Case was—

Well, she couldn't say just what Case was at the moment. She only knew she wasn't thrilled at seeing him talking so intimately with another woman, even if it was only Jill.

THOUGH JILL HAD to get back to the bank, Case lingered over coffee and dessert until the restaurant closed at two. It would reopen at five for the dinner hour. Maddie usually took advantage of those three hours to catch up on paperwork, shopping or other errands. Today, she had other things on her mind.

Hazel and the other lunch-hour waitress had already left. The kitchen staff was busily cleaning up lunch dishes and beginning to prepare for dinner under Mike's close supervision. Satisfied that everything was running smoothly, Maddie approached the table where Case still sat, sprawled in his chair with his fifth cup of coffee, obviously waiting for her.

"The restaurant is closed," she said.

He nodded. "Are you free for a while now?"

"Why?" she asked bluntly.

"I was hoping you could get away for an hour or so. There's something I want to show you."

"All right." She told herself she agreed for one reason only—she wanted to know what Jill and Case had discussed so avidly during lunch. Every time she'd looked their way during the busy shift, they'd had their heads close together. Jill had seemed to do most of the talking, but Case had certainly listened intently enough. And he'd smiled at Jill in a way that had made Maddie's hands curl into fists.

I'm not jealous, she assured herself. Only suspi-
ous.

Case looked a bit surprised by her easy acceptance.
stood quickly, as though afraid she would change
mind. "Let's go, then."

he motioned toward her short denim uniform. "I
e other clothes in the office. I could—"

You look fine," he assured her. "Do you need to tell
one you're leaving?"

laddie glanced toward the kitchen door to find her
er watching her with a smile. "No," she said wryly.
n't think that will be necessary."

se all but hustled her out of the restaurant. Mad-
lidn't even think to ask where he was taking her.
vas too busy trying to decide how to ask what Jill
aid to him.

DIE WAS only mildly surprised when Case drove
he long, winding driveway of the Fielding house.
is what you wanted to show me?"

nodded. "Jill mentioned that you'd never been
."

. I've seen the outside, of course. But—"

icked up the key this morning. I thought you
like to look around."

se—"

pressure, Maddie," he promised with a side-
lance at her. "I just want you to see it."

sighed.

house really was beautiful, she thought as Case
in the circular driveway. Though it could stand
f paint, the siding was a pale yellow, the deli-

cate gingerbread and other trim done in cream. The oval stained-glass window above the front porch reflected the afternoon sun, adding a bright touch of color to the Victorian facade.

She had to admit that she was curious about the inside, even though she couldn't help questioning Case's motives for bringing her here.

Maybe because Jill had already mentioned it, the first thing Maddie noticed about the house's interior was the strange color scheme. The carpeting was coral—a bit too orange for Maddie's taste—wall coverings and paint an odd mélange of pastels. It took her a moment to look beyond those details to the beauty of the floor plan.

"Case, it's wonderful," she breathed, noticing how much light streamed in through the oversize windows, how the glossy dark woods of trim and floors reflected that light even through the dust of a year's neglect. She pictured the octagonal dining room papered in a deep floral, with a crystal chandelier hanging from the bare wires that indicated where another chandelier had once hung. Obviously, the Fieldings had wanted to take that one with them. There was room for a long table, a buffet, a china cabinet.

"Nice place to entertain, isn't it?" Case asked.

"Lovely. Yet, oddly enough, the Fieldings were a very reclusive couple. They rarely had anyone over."

"There were only the two of them living here?"

Maddie nodded. "For the most part. Their sons and grandchildren visited occasionally."

Case shook his head. "This house was designed for a family," he said.

"Yet you're thinking of buying it just for yourself," Maddie couldn't resist saying.

"Ah, but I'm hoping to fill it with family," he reminded her.

She turned away to hide her blush and went off to explore the rest of the house.

Except for the colors, everything she found delighted her. She couldn't help exclaiming over each newly discovered detail, speculating aloud about what colors would best showcase the home's features and what furnishings would best suit the shape and size of each room. Case followed with a slight smile, occasionally nodding agreement or asking advice. "I'm not very good at decorating," he admitted. "I've only lived in prefurnished places before."

"You mean, you don't own any furnishings? No paintings or knickknacks or anything?" Maddie asked, unable to imagine someone his age not accumulating any personal mementos.

"No. Only my clothes and my car," he replied. "Looks like I'm going to have to start from scratch. Dishes, cookware, linens—hell, I don't even know what I'll need."

She turned to him, standing in the middle of the empty master bedroom. "Case, are you sure you want to go through with this?" she asked worriedly. "Are you aware of how much responsibility there is in maintaining a place like this? It must be four thousand square feet—"

"Four thousand, eight hundred and twenty-six," he corrected. "The agent supplied the specs."

"Even worse. It's been sitting here empty for a year. There may be roof leaks, plumbing and electrical problems, squirrels' nests in the attic and chimneys, pests, dry rot, for all you know. There are seven acres of grounds and fencing to keep up, the yard's a mess, the flower beds have gone to seed and the—"

"I'm aware of all that, Maddie," Case interrupted gently. "It's what I want."

She felt like throwing up her hands in exasperation. How could he sound so certain? So complacent?

He was walking away from everything he'd ever known, starting over with nothing in a strange town. He was fully prepared to marry her, whom he'd known only a matter of days, all told—or at least he *had* been ready to marry her when he'd arrived in Mitchell's Fork. She was assuming nothing had changed, since he'd seemed so anxious to show her this house.

The really unsettling part was that it wasn't at all hard for Maddie to imagine herself living in this house. Truth was, she loved it. All four thousand, eight hundred and twenty-six square feet of it. She almost itched to see it decorated and furnished.

But, she reminded herself, she still had no intention of giving up all her dreams of adventure to marry a man who wanted her only as a convenient wife and brood mare. And, as far as she could tell, that was exactly the way Case felt about her.

She needed so much more.

She crossed her arms defensively in front of her. "If you're so anxious to be tied down to all that responsibility, then I wish you luck," she said without emotion. "I think you'll soon grow tired of it."

"And I think you're wrong," he said evenly. "But if you're worried that the housework and maintenance chores will be too demanding to allow free time for travel and fun, don't be. Whenever we—I want time away, I can always hire someone to help out. Other people manage."

Because he'd managed to imply again that she would be living here with him, despite his promise not to pressure her, Maddie deliberately baited him. "You should bring Jill here," she suggested airily. "She loves this place."

Case watched her when he answered, as though trying to decide what she meant. "Yes, so she said. Though she mentioned that the color schemes weren't to her taste. I assured her they weren't mine, either."

"Great. Then the two of you have something in common. You really should ask her out, Case," Maddie said brittlely. "Jill's ready to settle down and quit her bank job. With your beautiful house and healthy finances, you shouldn't have any trouble sweeping her right off her feet."

Case frowned. "I thought Jill was your friend."

"She is my friend."

"Then why do you make her sound like a cheap gold digger?"

Maddie closed her eyes for a moment, feeling her face go hot. Oh, God, he was right. How could she have talked about Jill that way?

Okay, so maybe she *had* been a little jealous.

She must be losing her mind.

"I think we've seen everything here," she managed to say, her voice strained. "Maybe you'd better take me back to the restaurant now."

"Will you help m. here?"

"Help you? What do you mean?"

He motioned toward the pastel-flowered wallpaper. "As soon as the sale goes through, I'd like to start with the redecorating. I couldn't even begin to choose carpeting and paper and paints and furnishings alone. I'll need help. Will you?"

She felt her chest go even tighter at the thought of furnishing this house and then walking away from it—from him. "Case," she protested, "I'm really not all that good at that sort of thing. You could hire a professional decorator from Tupelo—"

He shook his head. "I don't want a professional decorator. I want this to be a home, not a glossy showplace."

"Then what about Jill? She's very talented with—"

"Jill seems very nice," Case interrupted flatly, taking a step closer. "I'm sure you and she are very good friends, despite what you've said this afternoon. But she's not the woman I want. I want you."

"To—er—help you decorate, you mean," she clarified, running her damp palms down her short denim skirt.

He paused a moment, then nodded. "That, too."

"Oh, Case—" She swallowed, then deliberately hardened her voice. "I'm not sure I'll be able to help much. It's going to take quite a while for you to get all this done. I'll probably be leaving town long before you've finished. I was looking at some travel brochures only yesterday, and—"

His hands fell gently on her shoulders, startling her into silence. "How long are you going to fight this, Maddie? How long are you going to keep pretending we don't belong together?"

"I'm not—"

He brushed her mouth with his own. "I want you, Maddie," he murmured. "I've wanted you for so damned long."

Her knees weakened. His arms felt so good around her, so right.

She could almost hear Jill's question from earlier. *Are you sure you don't want him, Maddie?*

She wanted him. She'd wanted him six months ago. She wanted him now.

The depth of her hunger terrified her.

"Case," she moaned.

"Maddie," he whispered, his lips moving against hers, his hands sliding slowly down her back to settle at her hips. He drew her closer, cradling her between his slightly spread thighs. She shivered as she felt the unmistakable hardness against her stomach.

She wasn't the only one who ached.

His hands tightened on her hips, and she felt the fine trembling in them with a sense of wonder. Somehow, she'd never thought she could make this hard, strong man tremble. The fact that she could stunned her.

She raised her gaze slowly to his face. His gray eyes blazed almost silver with heat, and a muscle worked in his jaw. He looked like a man in pain. She placed a cool hand on his cheek, feeling the heat of his skin. "You really do want me, don't you?" she murmured.

He groaned. "You have no idea. It's been so long . . ."

She blinked. "You mean, you haven't—er—for six months?"

"Longer than that," he corrected with a weak smile. "Quite a bit longer, actually."

"Heavens."

"I guess you—"

"It's been years," she said bluntly, then blushed.

He laughed softly, though the laughter was strained. "We're quite a pair, aren't we?"

"I don't take sex casually, Case."

"I know. Neither do I. I haven't in a very long time, anyway."

She was still locked against him, still all too vividly aware of his arousal. As well as her own. Their gazes held. Neither of them seemed to breathe.

Maddie realized how desperately important the next moments were to them. It was almost as though her entire future hung in the balance, to be decided with their next words. And she didn't have a clue what she wanted to say. What she hoped Case would say.

Case drew a deep, ragged breath. He kissed her quickly, roughly, then set her aside, releasing her with visible reluctance. "We'd better get back to the restaurant."

She kept her chin high, fighting an unexplainable disappointment. "Yes," she said. "I suppose we'd better."

Case paused in the spacious entryway before following Maddie out the front door. Glancing over her shoulder to see what was keeping him, she noted that he was just standing there, looking around him with what might have been longing.

She turned away quickly, swallowing a painful lump in her throat.

HAZEL WAS WAITING at the door of the restaurant when Case walked Maddie from the parking lot.

"Hazel?" Maddie said, studying her employee's expression with sudden misgiving. "Why are you back so early? I didn't expect you until almost five."

"Your daddy called me. He wants me and Bob to open the place tonight."

Something in Hazel's uncharacteristically gentle voice made Maddie go tense. "What is it? What's wrong?"

Case put a hand on her shoulder, as though aware of her fear.

"It's your grandpa, honey. They've taken him to the hospital. I'm sorry, but I'm afraid it's really bad."

Maddie sagged against Case, grateful when his arm went around her. "Oh, no," she whispered. "I have to go to him."

"I'll take you," Case said.

She didn't argue.

THE FAMILY had gathered in the hospital waiting room. Aunt Nettie's stern face was deeply lined with worry about her brother, the only remaining family member of her generation. Mike and Anita huddled together in one corner, holding hands as they awaited news of their father's condition. Dan stood behind his wife, one hand resting supportively on her shoulder, his broad face grave. Lisa and her teenagers sat crowded together on a small vinyl bench. Kathy was crying silently, while Jeff leafed through a magazine with mechanical movements that suggested he was hardly seeing the words in front of him.

All turned to greet them when Maddie and Case entered the room. Mike came forward and took his daughter's hands.

"How is he?" she asked, her voice tremulous.

Mike shook his head. "We don't know yet, honey. But—it doesn't look good."

She moaned, and Mike took her in his arms. "We can only hope for the best," he murmured.

"I know," Maddie whispered, blinking back tears she refused to shed yet. She knew her grandfather had been in failing health for some time, but she loved him dearly. She would miss him very much if they lost him now.

During the next hour, family members drew strength from one another. Case remained with them, fetching coffee, talking quietly to Jeff, soothing Kathy with an ease that would have surprised Maddie had she not been too concerned about her grandfather to give it much thought.

Leaving Kathy talking with her grandmother, Case moved to stand beside Maddie. "How are you holding up?" he asked quietly.

"I'm okay," she assured him wearily. "I just wish we would hear something."

He slid an arm around her shoulders. "There's probably nothing they can tell you yet."

"I know. I just . . ." Her voice trailed away.

His arm tightened. "I know," he said roughly. "I'm sorry."

She couldn't resist the urge to rest her cheek on his shoulder. He was so warm, so strong. Just for that moment, she assured herself, she needed his strength.

8

WORD OF THE CRISIS soon got around. A steady stream of well-wishers passed through the waiting room. Medical staff who knew the family personally. Two ministers. Friends from their church and community.

Feeling very much the outsider, Case stood on the fringe of the subdued crowd, watching as Maddie hugged nearly everyone who visited, and thanked each one gratefully for being there. He knew she was tired, and wondered how she could be so gracious when she must be half-sick with worry. But then he realized that she needed the support she was drawing from these visitors.

This was her family, he thought with a touch of wonder. Not just the ones related by blood, but the friends and neighbors who shared her history, her past.

Despite all her talk about needing to get away from Mitchell's Fork, and needing more adventure than she could find within the boundaries of the little town, Maddie belonged here. This was her home.

He wondered wistfully if there would ever be a place for him there.

He stiffened when Jackson Babbit showed up, looking like a dude-ranch lounge singer in a garishly printed Western shirt and skintight jeans with overly glossy boots, his dark hair moussed into a careful back-sweep.

Babbit headed straight to Maddie, who went into his arms with an ease that made Case's teeth clench.

Reminding himself of the circumstances, he made an effort to relax. Maddie was hugging the guy like a friend, he told himself. Not at all the way she'd molded herself against Case only a short while before.

Because his understanding only stretched so far, Case allowed them only a few moments alone before he moved to Maddie's side. He slid an arm around her waist, subtly but effectively drawing her away from the other man.

"Doing okay?" he asked her again, noting how pale she looked. How tired.

She nodded. "Yes, Case, thank you."

"Want some more coffee?"

She started to shake her head, then changed her mind. "Yes, I think I do," she said.

"I'll get it," Jackson offered promptly, clearly studying the way Maddie leaned into Case's side. "Anyone else want any?" he asked, moving around the room with the offer.

Glad the guy was gone, Case stayed close to Maddie after that, even when Babbit returned with a tray of steaming foam cups. Jill had appeared from somewhere, and she helped Babbit pass out the hot beverages.

Another half hour passed before the doctor finally appeared with news.

"Looks like he's going to pull through," the paunchy, balding physician announced. "He gave us quite a scare, though. We'll have to watch him closely for the next few days."

Maddie turned and buried her face in Case's chest. Holding her closely, he could feel the shudder of relief pass through her. It was all he could do not to kiss her then. He resisted only because he knew it would embarrass her for him to do so this publicly.

She remained there only a moment before she pulled away, gave him a quick smile of gratitude and turned to hug her father. And then she rushed over to Nettie, who'd begun to cry for the first time now that she knew her brother would survive.

"Good news, isn't it?" a voice asked from behind Case.

He turned to find Jackson Babbit standing nearby. "Yes," Case said, a bit stiffly. "It is good news. I hope there isn't a relapse."

"Yeah. Doc Adcock sounded pretty confident that everything would be okay, though."

"Mmm." Case was still watching Maddie, who was surrounded now by family and friends, looking as though she would be busy for quite some time.

"Maddie's probably going to be tied up here for a while," Jackson said as though he'd heard Case's thoughts. "How about you and me go have us a drink? Relax with a beer or two?"

Surprised at the suggestion, Case lifted an eyebrow. "I thought this was a dry county," he said noncommittally.

"There's a private club with a liquor license only a couple of blocks from here. I'm a member."

Case searched the guy's bland smile, wondering what the hell he wanted. He figured the easiest way to find out in this case was simply to ask. "Why would you want to have a drink with me?"

Babbit shrugged. "Word is you're planning to settle down here. We'll probably be seeing each other around quite a bit. I figured we might as well get to know each other."

After thinking about it a moment, Case decided to agree. This was the man Maddie had been seeing. Now seemed like a good time to let Babbit know that Maddie was no longer available.

"All right," he said. "I'll tell Maddie we're leaving."

Babbit looked a bit surprised that Case had taken him up on the offer, but he nodded.

Maddie looked even more surprised than Babbit when Case drew her away from her chattering family for a moment to tell her why he was leaving. "You're going to have a drink with Jackson?" she repeated as though she wasn't sure she'd heard him correctly.

"Yeah. Looks as though you're going to be busy here for a while. I don't want to get in your way."

"But . . . you and Jackson, er—"

"Yes?" He waited patiently for her to complete the sentence.

Maddie sighed. "Never mind. I don't think this is a great idea, but it's certainly none of my business who you have a drink with."

Case smiled. "Don't worry. I'll be on my best behavior."

She snorted inelegantly. "Sure. And if I believe that, you have some land to sell me, right?"

"A house and seven acres, actually. And it's not for sale—it's a gift."

She flushed. "Case—"

He recognized that you're-pushing-me-again tone. He held up a hand to reassure her. "That's all. Go take care of your family, Maddie. I'll call you later, okay?"

She nodded. "All right." She half turned away, then stopped and looked over her shoulder. "Case?"

He'd been watching her. "Yes?"

She seemed to grope for words for a moment before saying, "Thank you. You know, for being here with me this afternoon."

Case smiled and touched her cheek. "This is where I belong," he said quietly.

And then he left, before she felt the need to protest his certainty that he and Maddie were already committed to being together—in good times and bad, as far as he was concerned.

JACKSON WALKED into the dimly lighted club with the ease of a frequent visitor, an impression reinforced by the casual greetings he received from the staff and the few other patrons relaxing there on that Tuesday evening. A large-screen TV played in one corner, tuned to a baseball game on the sports network. Several men watched intently, two of them involved in a noisy but apparently good-natured argument about which team would end up in the championship slot.

The only women in the place seemed to be waiting tables, though Jackson assured Case it wasn't an all-male club. "There just aren't many women who come here on weeknights," he explained as he motioned Case into a booth. "They tend to show up on weekends, when there's live music and dancing rather than sports."

"Maddie ever come here to dance?" Case asked, sitting down and glancing at the small dance floor and imagining himself there, swaying to sultry music with Maddie in his arms.

"I've brought her a couple of times," Babbit answered airily, making Case scowl as he was replaced in the mental picture by this moussed-and-bejeweled joker.

"Hey, Jackson. Howzit goin'?" a bleached blonde in tight jeans and a sequined Western shirt asked as she approached the booth.

"Good as always, Joannie. You met Case, here, yet?"

"No. How ya' doin', Case? I'm Joannie," she said unnecessarily. Her smile was broad and friendly.

Case nodded. "Pleasure to meet you," he murmured.

"Oooh. The guy's even got manners. So how come he's hanging out with a lowlife like you, eh, Jackson?" she teased.

"He's new in town. Don't know any better yet," Jackson retorted.

"Case, honey, you and me have got to have a long talk," Joannie said gravely. "This boy'll get you in hot water for sure if you stay around him too long."

Case glanced from Joannie to Jackson and back again. "Troublemaker, is he?"

She sighed and shook her head. "The worst kind. But ain't nothing the love of a good woman couldn't fix."

Jackson laughed. "Honey, I been married to two good women and neither of them had any luck."

She shook a playful finger at him. "Never give up, I say. When you going to bring Maddie around again, hmm?"

Jackson made a production of loudly clearing his throat. "Did I mention that Case is Maddie's fiancé?"

Wide-eyed, Joannie whipped her head around to stare at Case. "You and Maddie are getting married?"

Again, it was Jackson who answered before Case could speak. "I didn't say they were getting married," he corrected. "Case just calls himself her fiancé. Last I heard, Maddie didn't seem to agree."

"She'll come around," Case murmured, looking at Jackson. The words were a warning.

Jackson's grin never wavered. "We'll just have to see about that, won't we?"

"Oh, Lord," Joannie moaned, rolling her eyes upward. "You two start breaking furniture or anything, and I'm going to get blamed for it. I just know it."

"We promise not to break any furniture," Case assured her, smiling at her dramatics.

"You notice he didn't say anything about arms or legs," Jackson murmured.

Joannie giggled. "So, are y'all going to order or just sit here stacking chips on your shoulders and daring each other to knock 'em off?"

"Beer," Jackson said promptly.

"Make it two," Case added.

Joannie nodded. "Behave yourself 'til I get back, you hear?" she warned. And then she giggled again. "I wouldn't want to miss anything juicy."

"She seems nice," Case commented when Joannie had bounced away. Maybe he could convince Jackson to pursue the blonde and leave Maddie alone, he thought.

Jackson's smile faded as he looked after the waitress. "She *is* nice," he agreed. "Poor kid."

"Poor kid?"

"Yeah. Her husband broke his back in a fall last year. Now he's in a wheelchair and they've got three little kids to support. Joannie's working two jobs, but they're having a hard time making ends meet, with his medical bills and all."

"Damn." Case watched Joannie trade quips with a man at the bar as she filled two mugs with foaming beer. He thought of how much pain she must be hiding behind her contagious smile.

"Yeah. The townsfolk have been real good to help them out, of course, but Bud—Joannie's husband—is the proud type. He doesn't like to accept charity."

"Not even for his kids?"

"*Only* for his kids," Jackson corrected.

Joannie slid the mugs in front of them, along with a bowl of peanuts. "Get you guys anything else?"

"Not now, thank you," Case replied.

Joannie smiled. "Such nice manners," she repeated. "You could learn something from him, Jackson." And then she hurried away in answer to a summons from one of the baseball fans.

Case made a mental note to tip generously when he left.

Jackson took a sip of his beer, popped a few peanuts in his mouth and chewed in silence for a moment. Then he said, "I'm glad Maddie's grandfather is going to pull through. They're a real tight-knit family. He won't be around much longer, I guess, but I know they're grateful for whatever time they have left with him."

Case had never known his own grandparents. His mother had died when he was seven—he hardly remembered her now—and he'd never known his father. He'd lived in a series of foster homes until he was eighteen, when he'd graduated from high school and declared his independence. Rootless and reckless, he'd been excellent material for undercover law enforcement.

Remembering the way Maddie's family had drawn together in their fear and grief earlier that evening, he wondered if he would ever know that sort of familial connection. It was what he wanted—but his inexperience with close family ties felt like a definite disadvantage at the moment.

"I'm going to marry her," he said suddenly, with a touch of defiance that was aimed at himself as much as Babbit.

"You're scaring her."

Case was startled by Babbit's comment, which was definitely not the response he'd expected. "She has no reason to be afraid of me."

"She thinks she does. She thinks you'll hurt her again."

Case cleared his throat. "She told you what happened in Cancún?"

"That you left her standing at the altar, so to speak? Yeah, she told me."

"I told her why I had to leave. I had no choice."

Babbit shrugged. "She's convinced herself you did her a favor by leaving when you did."

"She's wrong."

"Mmm." Babbit took another long draw of his beer.

Case had hardly touched his own. He cradled the mug loosely between his hands as he searched Babbit's overly bland expression. He couldn't quite understand the guy—was he competition or ally? Friend or foe? "You aren't hoping to marry her yourself, are you?" he asked warily.

Babbit shuddered. "I've been married twice. That's more punishment than any man should have to take."

"Then what do you want from her?"

"Maddie's my friend, Brannigan. I like her, and I respect her. I can't say that about many people. I don't want to see her hurt."

"I won't be leaving her at the altar again."

"There are other ways you could hurt her. Taking her for granted, for example."

"I wouldn't do that."

"You already have."

Case started to argue, then fell silent. *Had* he taken it for granted that Maddie would marry him if he simply refused to accept any other answer? He'd been so sure, so confident that he'd made an offer on a house—without even asking her if she liked the place. Of course, he knew she *did* like it; she hadn't been able to hide her approval when he'd shown her through it that afternoon. But he'd already made the offer.

He tugged at the collar of his shirt. "It hasn't been intentional," he muttered. He didn't like explaining himself to this guy—but Babbit was Maddie's friend. It wouldn't hurt to have him on his side.

"Maybe not," Babbit said. "But if I were you, I'd start thinking about how Maddie might be feeling, and less about what you want. If not, you're going to lose her."

The very possibility of losing Maddie made Case's stomach clench. His hands tightened around the beer mug. "Why are you telling me this?" he asked bluntly.

Jackson looked thoughtful. "I'm not sure," he admitted. "But I know Maddie wouldn't be happy leaving town by herself, traipsing around Europe—or anyplace else—alone. She's the family type. She thrives on connections.

"Oh, she's been restless and a little bored lately—maybe because she's turning thirty soon and feels like she hasn't experienced much. But I'm afraid she isn't ready for the sort of experience she'd find if she left Mitchell's Fork unprepared. She's smart, and she's tough when she has to be, and she's been taking care of herself, her family and the restaurant for several years. But she's vulnerable. Look what happened the last time she went off by herself. Almost got herself married to a stranger."

Case was embarrassed to feel his cheeks grow warm. Hearing his own thoughts so eerily echoed by Jackson Babbit made him uncomfortable; being used as an example of the perils awaiting Maddie made him angry. "I told you, that wouldn't have been a mistake. Maddie and I were meant to find each other."

"I'm not the one you need to convince of that," Jackson told him.

"You're right. So why am I wasting my breath?" Case muttered disgruntledly.

"You look to me like a guy who could use a friend."

Case frowned. Of course he wanted friends in Mitchell's Fork. After all, he planned to make this his home. But...Jackson Babbit? He studied the other man's hairdo and clothes, thinking what an odd pair he and Jackson made. And then he remembered the man's loyal defense of Maddie and obvious sympathy for Joannie.

Maybe the guy wasn't as bad as he first appeared. Maybe that was what Maddie liked about him.

"A man can always use more friends," he said carefully.

"Just one question. Who's the greatest singer of all time?"

"George Jones," Case answered promptly, both from personal choice and because Babbit's taste wasn't hard to guess.

Babbit grinned. "Drinks are on me," he said. "Hey, Joannie. Bring us another round, okay?"

IT WAS LATE that evening when Maddie finally had a chance to see her grandfather. He lay in the hospital bed, looking frail and weak and very old. She blinked back a sheen of tears as she leaned over the bed and kissed his bald head. "Hello, Grampa."

"Maddie," he said, his voice whispery-soft. "What are you doing here? Shouldn't you be out with your young man?"

She smiled. "And which young man would that be?"

"Your betrothed, that's who. I like him, girl. He's got steady eyes."

Maddie held her smile with an effort. "I'll tell him you said so." This was not the time to remind her grandfather that she still didn't consider herself officially "betrothed." "How are you feeling?"

He sighed. "Tuckered out."

"I'll let you rest, then. I'll see you tomorrow, all right?"

He nodded. "I'll be here."

"I know. The doctor says you'll have to stay in the hospital a few more days."

Her grandfather's thin fingers tightened around her hand. "I thought I was going to be joining Annabelle this time."

Maddie's smile quivered. "I'm very selfish, Grampa. I'm not ready to let you go just yet."

"Guess I'll hang around for a while longer, then," he said gruffly. "Now go on home, Maddie. A pretty girl has better things to do with her evenings than to hang around a hospital."

"I love you, Grampa."

He patted her hand and smiled, his thin, blue-veined eyelids already closing.

ACCOMPANIED BY Jill, Maddie went back to the restaurant after leaving the hospital to make sure everything had gone smoothly during the dinner hour. Hazel and the other staff assured her they'd gotten along just fine without Maddie and Mike that evening. Business had been light, they said, but no more than usual for a weeknight.

Jill followed Maddie into the restaurant office after Maddie locked the front doors. "I still can't believe Case went out for drinks with Jackson," she said. "What I wouldn't give to have been a fly beneath their table!"

Maddie pretended to concentrate on the paperwork on her desk. "They're just getting to know each other. It's not so strange—two single guys of about the same age with nothing else to do on a Tuesday evening."

"Two single guys who are after the same woman," Jill reminded her wickedly.

Maddie flushed. "Don't be ridiculous. Jackson isn't 'after' me. We're friends, that's all, and you know it. As for Case—"

"You aren't going to try to tell me Case isn't after you, are you?"

"No," Maddie sighed. "I won't try to tell you that. I think Case has made himself clear enough."

"Mmm. As far as that guy's concerned, you've got a red X painted on your forehead. You're marked. Targeted."

"I'm convenient," Maddie muttered.

Jill seemed surprised by Maddie's choice of words. "You think that's all it is?"

Maddie shrugged.

Jill shook her head. "I don't think so. You're hardly 'convenient,' Maddie. Look at how much trouble you've given him since he came to town. And there are other women who wouldn't bother resisting him."

"Like you?"

Jill shrugged. "Maybe, if he were available. He's not, though. The guy's not interested in anyone but you."

Maddie cleared her throat and murmured something noncommittal.

"Is that why you're resisting him so ferociously?" Jill asked a moment later. "You think he wants to marry you for the wrong reasons?"

To avoid meeting her friend's too-perceptive eyes, Maddie kept her gaze focused on the paperwork. "I know why he wants to marry me. He wants a wife. Kids. A home."

"And love?"

"It hasn't been mentioned," Maddie said stiffly.

"Oh." Jill seemed to suddenly understand. "I didn't realize . . ."

"It doesn't matter," Maddie said quickly, determined to hide her own feelings—at least as much as she could hide them from someone who'd known her since kindergarten. "I still think Case will be gone in a month, if not less. He'll be bored out of his mind by then. Can you really see a man like Case settling into the routines around here?"

Jill thought about it a moment before answering. "It does seem unlikely that a man who's accustomed to danger would be content with a weekly Little League game for excitement."

"And he's never owned a home," Maddie said, ignoring the pang that went through her at Jill's concurrence. "He has no idea how boring routine maintenance can be. He's probably never even mowed a lawn."

"I bet he's never been to a PTA meeting, either. Remember those long, dull programs we had to sit through with our parents? My dad hated them. He used to make all these crazy excuses to get out of going without Mom getting mad at him. Not that he ever got away with any of them."

"Exactly," Maddie said, warming to her subject. "And as far as cultural entertainment, the Royale Theater is the best we have to offer. Two movies a month, both of which have already been playing for weeks everywhere else in the country. It's a two-hour drive to the nearest live theater or symphony or ballet or professional sports stadium."

"Right. You and I only get to any of those things once every six weeks or so. A guy who's accustomed to having entertainment at his fingertips would have a hard time dealing with that."

Maddie nodded. "That's exactly what I mean."

"Something tells me Case would learn to adapt," Jill said with a smile.

Sighing, Maddie threw up her hands in a gesture of frustration. "I thought you were beginning to see my side."

"Oh, I see it. I'm just not so sure you're right. So, how did you like the house?"

Maddie was confused for a moment.

"Case told me he was going to take you out to the Fielding place when you finished your lunch shift," Jill explained. "I told him you'd never seen the interior, and that it might be a good idea for him to find out if you liked it before he put any money down on it."

"You said that to him? Honestly, Jill—"

"I know. I'm a traitor and a lowlife worm. But how *did* you like the house? Did you agree with me about the colors?"

"Of course. The colors are terrible. But the house—"

"Great, isn't it?"

"It has potential," Maddie said slowly. "But I—"

"Case said he wanted you to help him decorate it. I envy you. I'd love to get my hands on a place like that."

"Fine. Volunteer to take my place."

Jill shook her head. "I already did. I'm telling you, Maddie, the guy wants you or no one. If I were you, I wouldn't be so quick to dismiss his feelings for you. Something tells me you're underestimating him."

Maddie didn't agree. But, remembering how tenderly Case had held her in the hospital waiting room, she didn't want to argue about him anymore just then. She had needed him, and he had been there for her—this time. She knew that all too quickly, she would become addicted to having him there for her.

But how long could she expect it to last? How long before he grew tired of her, and of Mitchell's Fork, and left her heartbroken? Again.

She knew what Case wanted from the marriage he had in mind—what he thought he needed from such a union. But what about what she wanted? What about her needs?

Case had offered her a lovely home and financial security. Though Maddie was aware that some women would be content to settle for those, she needed much, much more. Love. Commitment. Unwavering loyalty and devotion. A lifetime partnership.

Was Case really prepared to offer all that? And if he did, could Maddie really trust him to keep his promises?

She swallowed a moan, deeply afraid that she would be willing to take that risk for Case. If only there was some way to be sure of just how much she meant to him.

9

WITHIN TWO WEEKS, Case had moved into his house. The sale hadn't gone through that quickly, of course, though his offer was immediately accepted. Undeterred by the slow-moving system, Case had contacted the former owners and arranged to move into the house as a tenant until the final papers were signed transferring the deed to him. He'd had all he could stand of the tiny motel room.

He saw Maddie several times during those two weeks, though not as often as he would have liked. He made himself stay away from her for days at a time, and made an effort to call each time before coming to see her. Though he missed her every minute he wasn't with her, ached to touch her, hold her—and more—he was determined to give her no reason to accuse him of taking her for granted.

He immersed himself in the daily routines of Mitchell's Fork. He quickly learned that breakfast at the Classy Café on Main Street was a valued tradition among the town's old-timers. There, he drank coffee strong enough to strip paint, ordered eggs, bacon, biscuits and gravy, and listened to the stories told by retirees who enjoyed having someone new to share them with. He was still a newcomer, still an outsider, but he was welcomed warmly at the café. That pleased him, despite the avid curiosity lurking behind the greetings.

He had his hair cut by a garrulous barber at the Main Street Barbershop, which had been in business since 1922. He couldn't help noticing that most of the magazines provided for the customers were almost as old as the shop. His no-nonsense haircut came with a free side order of corny jokes and local gossip. Case got a kick out of both.

He opened an account at the bank. Maddie's friend Jill introduced him to Mr. Peacock, the bank president. At first a bit suspicious, Peacock took one look at the amount Case was transferring to the bank in Mitchell's Fork and immediately decided they would be best friends for life. He invited Case to be his guest at the Rotary luncheon every Thursday in the private dining room at Mike and Maddie's Restaurant. Case promptly accepted.

Everywhere he went, he received advice on how best to "court" Maddie Carmichael. It seemed the townsfolk had been worried about Maddie.

"Almost thirty and still unmarried," said one of the old gentlemen at the Classy Café. "It ain't natural for a pretty little thing like that. Too picky, that's what I've always told her daddy. None of the boys around here pleased her. 'Cept for Jackson Babbit, of course. And everyone knows he won't marry her. After those last two wives of his cleaned him out, that boy looks at matrimony like a chicken looks at a stew pot."

"You can't let her manipulate you. I always told her daddy he was spoilin' her," an elderly woman stated. "After her mama died, weren't nothing her daddy didn't give her if she wanted it. Made her think she was above herself. Now she's dyin' her hair and wearin' them tight clothes and runnin' around with that Babbit boy, and I can tell you her mama would turn over in her grave if she saw her. 'Course, she can be a sweet little thing. Takes real good care of her grandpa and her great-aunt Nettie. Lots of young people don't have time for their elders these days. Don't you keep her away from her family, Case Brannigan, you hear?"

"Maddie Carmichael's going to make someone a good wife and mother," Hank the barber said pointedly. "She comes from a good family, knows how to cook and run a household. Smart, too. Graduated top of her class from Mitchell's Fork High and then went on to business school to learn about keeping the books for the restaurant. Some folks been saying she's getting out of hand, but I say she just needs herself a man and some young'uns to keep her busy. You know what I'm talking about, Brannigan?"

"Romance," Jill whispered as she slipped Case his first set of temporary checks on his newly opened bank account. "Try flowers and poetry and soft music. Maddie's a real pushover for romance."

"Diamonds," Peacock said, with an eye on Case's bank balance. "If you want her to feel engaged, you've got to get a rock on her finger. My brother owns a jewelry store, you know. I'll introduce you at the Rotary meeting. He can make you a deal."

Case politely thanked everyone for their suggestions, and continued to pursue his own course of action. But—just in case—he kept a mental note of everything they'd said to him.

He just might get desperate before this was over, he thought ruefully.

MADDIE TURNED her car into the long driveway leading to Case's house. A stack of thick wallpaper sample books lay in the passenger seat, and there were carpet samples in the back seat. The samples had come from the local hardware store and decorating center. She still wasn't quite sure how she'd ended up agreeing to bring them with her on this Monday afternoon in June.

She just didn't seem to be able to say no when Case asked her a favor. It was that very weakness that had almost gotten her married to the guy.

She saw Case as soon as the house came into view. He was kneeling by the steps leading to the front porch, swinging a hammer with more enthusiasm than skill. He was wearing jeans and sneakers, but he'd taken off his shirt. The afternoon sun filtered through the leaves of the massive oak tree that stood to one side of the house, making a rippling pattern of light and shadows on Case's glistening back.

Maddie swallowed hard. *Oh, heavens.*

Case looked around when Maddie climbed out of her car and slammed the door. He set down the hammer and jumped to his feet, welcoming her with a smile that only stoked the heat building somewhere deep inside her. "Hi," he said, his tone making the casual syllable almost an endearment.

"Hi," she managed to say in return. She quickly moved around the car and opened the passenger door. "I brought the samples."

Case pulled on a blue chambray shirt as he approached her, though he left it hanging loose and unbuttoned over his jeans. "I really appreciate this, Maddie. I need your advice."

"For what it's worth," Maddie said self-deprecatingly. She lifted the load of wallpaper books and turned to hand them to him. As she faced him, she couldn't resist glancing down at the skin revealed by the open front of his shirt. She hadn't seen his bare chest since they'd swam together in Cancún. She remembered how tanned and muscular he was, how—

Maddie gasped. The wallpaper books hit the ground with a heavy thud as she covered her mouth with suddenly trembling hands.

Case reached out to her in confusion. "Maddie? What is it?"

Her gaze was focused low on his stomach. Without stopping to think about what she was doing, she pulled his shirt out of the way, then walked slowly around him, lifting the fabric to expose his lower back.

"Oh, my God," she moaned. "Oh, Case."

It was the first time she'd seen the scars. Just above the loose waistband of his low-slung jeans, the large entry scar was still red and puckered, an angry-looking testimony to the shot that had almost incapacitated him. From its placement, Maddie could tell that the bullet had missed his spine by only an inch or so. The crooked red scars she'd spotted low on his side had been the exit wounds, she realized with a sickening jolt.

She thought of his leg, and the limp that had been steadily improving since he'd arrived in Mitchell's Fork three weeks ago. There must be an equally ugly scar on his thigh, she realized, her heart twisting at this evidence of the pain he'd suffered. For some reason, his story hadn't been quite real to her until now, when she saw the evidence with her own eyes.

Case glanced downward and scowled. "Sorry. I know it looks bad. I'll button my shirt."

Hardly hearing him, she reached out to touch the damaged skin with unsteady fingertips. "It must have hurt you so horribly."

"It wasn't pleasant," he said, making the understatement in a flat monotone. "But the scars will fade, in time."

She shook her head irritably. "I don't care about the scars," she said fiercely.

Case studied her face for a moment. And then he stepped over the scattered wallpaper books and took her in his arms.

Maddie buried her face in his bare shoulder, her hands sliding up his back beneath his shirt. "I'm so sorry," she whispered. "Because you were hurt, and because I treated you so badly when you tried to tell me about it. I didn't know— I didn't realize—"

"I know," he murmured into her hair. "I know, Maddie. It's okay."

For the first time, she allowed herself to think about him lying in a hospital bed, uncertain of whether he would walk again. He must have been scared, and lonely—had he thought of her?

She swallowed a moan. This was exactly the reason she hadn't allowed herself to think about what he'd told her. She'd known even then that she couldn't think of Case in pain without softening toward him.

"Maddie," Case said, tilting her head upward with a finger beneath her chin. "The wounds will heal. The scars will fade. It's over."

But it wasn't over, she mused, studying his so-familiar face. He was here, still intent on marrying her and living with her in this house. And she still didn't know whether he loved her, or was just enamored of the idea of all she represented.

She still wasn't even sure what she felt toward him. She wanted him. She was fascinated by him, had been from the beginning. She couldn't bear to think of him in pain. And no matter what she'd said to him or to anyone else, she couldn't really imagine telling him goodbye and walking away from him, never to see him again. She feared that doing so would break her already battered heart.

Was this love?

She glumly suspected that it was.

"You look so serious," he murmured, caressing her cheek. "What are you thinking?"

"I'm wondering what I'm going to do about you," she said as she had once before.

"Marry me," he said, repeating his earlier reply.

She only sighed.

He smiled a bit crookedly and lowered his head to kiss her. "Let's go look at wallpaper samples," he said when he finally released her mouth.

Still reeling from his kiss, Maddie nodded mutely, gathered an armload of carpet squares from the back seat, and followed him into his house.

IT WAS the first time Maddie had been inside the house since Case had shown it to her two weeks ago, the day her grandfather had taken ill. She was amused to see that it was almost as empty now as it had been then.

Case had apparently been sleeping in a sleeping bag in the den. Two suitcases and a duffel bag were scattered nearby, the contents spilling out of them. His wardrobe, she realized.

"This is really all you own?" she couldn't resist asking.

He shrugged. "Yeah. I have a lot of things I need to buy now. I don't even have hangers for my shirts."

"Furnishing a house this size is going to be a major undertaking," she warned him.

"I thought I'd just do a few rooms at a time. Add things as I need them," he explained. "But it seemed like a good idea to paint and wallpaper and recarpet before I bring any furniture in."

"I suppose so—if you don't mind living this way in the meantime."

He shrugged again. "I've lived in more primitive surroundings."

She wondered again what kind of life he'd led. How could staid Mitchell's Fork ever compare?

Case set the stack of wallpaper books on the floor and motioned for Maddie to do the same with the carpet samples. "Want something cold to drink?" he offered.

"That sounds nice. Thank you." She followed him into the kitchen.

There was a stack of paper plates on the bar. The kitchen had come furnished with a large, built-in refrigerator, stove, oven, microwave and dishwasher. Case had added an electric coffeemaker. As far as Maddie could tell, that was about it.

"What have you been eating?" she asked.

He opened the refrigerator door. She could see luncheon meats, a jar of mustard, canned drinks, a gallon of milk and several foil-covered casserole dishes. "Almost every evening, someone stops by with a casserole of some sort. I think your friend Jill is behind it. She brought one the first night I moved in—some sort of chicken dish. It was good."

Maddie fought against that unbecoming jealousy again. "So Jill came to see you, did she?"

"Mmm. Real neighborly of her, I thought. The others, too, of course."

"Wasn't it, though."

Maddie thought she saw a smile tugging at the corners of Case's mouth when he ducked his head into the refrigerator. "What will you have?" he asked, his voice bland. "Cola, beer, juice?"

Maddie asked for a cola.

"You'll have to drink it out of the can or from a coffee mug," he warned. "I don't have any drinking glasses."

"The can's fine," Maddie assured him. She moved to the sink and looked out the window above it. The covered porch wrapped around that side of the house, with a ragged flower bed on the other side. She pictured lush ferns hanging from the porch eaves, and brightly colored flowers blooming in the bed. It would make a nice view for someone working in this kitchen, she thought, carefully keeping any personal references out of the silent observation.

"I hear you've been getting to know the townspeople," she said without turning around. "Seems like everyone I run in to these days asks about you. You've made quite a hit down at the Classy Café."

"Great breakfast," he said, moving to stand beside her. He handed her the soft drink and popped the opener on his drink. "The people around here seem nice, for the most part."

Hearing an undertone in his voice, she glanced at him. "You've met some who weren't so nice?"

His eyes narrowed. "Met your sheriff this morning."

She winced. "McAdams? How did you run in to him? You haven't been getting into trouble already, have you?"

"Not exactly. I went into his office to report a crime. He's a real idiot, isn't he?"

"Yes. What crime did you report?" She turned to him in curiosity.

A flicker of anger lighted his gray eyes. "Some bastard keyed my Ferrari."

"Keyed it?" she repeated, not quite sure what he meant.

"Yeah. Took a key and scraped it down both sides of my car. Left gouges from front to back on both sides. I was really pissed off."

Maddie already knew Case well enough to know how he felt about that car—his only extravagance, he'd called it. "I can imagine. When did it happen?"

"While I was having breakfast."

"I don't suppose anyone saw who did it."

Case growled. "Not that they'd admit."

She cocked her head. "You think someone did see?"

"Yeah. A couple of people I asked acted pretty funny—like they wanted to tell me, but were afraid to."

Maddie had a sudden sinking feeling. "Oh."

"Yeah." Case seemed to think that she'd come to the same conclusion he had. "I think it was that Cooper kid and his punk friends. I wish I'd caught the little jerks in the act."

"You're probably right," Maddie said. "It sounds like something Danny would do, especially since he seems to have taken a dislike to you. You won't get anyone to testify against him, though."

"That's what your idiot sheriff said when I told him who I suspected. Said he didn't have any proof and there wasn't anything he could do about it. He implied that it was my fault for having such an expensive car in the first place."

Maddie exclaimed in disgust. "The jerk."

"That's pretty much what I called him. With a few choice adjectives, of course."

Now Maddie was worried. "Case, if you're serious about settling here, you really don't want to make an enemy of the sheriff or the Coopers. They can make it unpleasant for you here, to say the least."

"They don't worry me."

"I know you aren't afraid of them, and I understand. But—well, just don't do anything to make the townspeople have to choose sides, okay? After all, you're a stranger to them, even though they seem to like what they know of you. The Coopers have lived here for years, and they have a lot of power."

"Only because no one's had the guts to stand up to them."

"Maybe. But I still wish you'd be careful."

He gave her his familiar shrug. "Whatever you say, Maddie."

He always said that in a tone that implied he didn't agree with a word of what she said, Maddie thought with exasperation. She'd tried to warn him about making enemies of the Coopers and their cronies. That was the most she could do for now.

Turning away from the window, she moved past him toward the den. "Maybe we should get started with those carpet and wallpaper samples," she said.

LACKING ANYWHERE ELSE to sit, they sat cross-legged on the too-orange carpet on the den floor, the samples spread in front of them, their heads close together as they bent over them.

Maddie was secretly surprised by Case's participation in the selection process. He offered more opinions and suggestions than she'd expected, and had very definite ideas about what he did not want. "No birds and no plaids," he said flatly. "I don't like wallpaper with birds or plaids."

Maddie giggled. "How about plaid birds?"

He gave her a mock scowl. "Cute." He pointed to a tasteful floral pattern done in dark greens and burgundies. "I like that."

"So do I," she admitted, picturing it in the dining room. "Are these the colors you want to use?"

"I like blue and green and red. I don't like pink or purple."

She bit her lip. "That narrows it down," she admitted unsteadily.

Case looked at her suspiciously. "Are you making fun of me?"

"Heaven forbid."

"You are." He sounded resigned. "Would you rather do this without me?"

"Of course not," she said quickly. "It's your house."

"You know I'm hoping it will be *our* house."

She looked steadily at the samples in front of her. "You said you wouldn't do that."

"I said I'd try not to push," he reminded her. "I never said I would lie."

"Case," she groaned. "You make this so difficult for me."

"Good," he said roughly, reaching for her. "Because it's damned difficult for me not to remind you every day that we should already be married. That we should be living here together now, furnishing our house, getting it ready for our kids."

Her hands settled on his shoulders—only to steady herself, she thought. "Case. Don't."

"Maddie," he mocked her gently. "I can't help it."

His mouth closed over hers with a hunger that he'd held in restraint for the past two weeks.

Maddie could almost feel her common sense slip away. Even worse, she did absolutely nothing to hold on to it.

He'd buttoned his shirt since they'd entered the house. Maddie found herself resenting the fabric that kept her hands from his skin.

The too-orange carpet that she'd so disliked proved surprisingly soft and comfortable when he lowered her to it. He leaned over her, pressing her more deeply into it. She arched up to meet him, her mouth moving avidly beneath his.

Case plunged his hands into her hair, holding her still as he devoured her mouth, again and again. They writhed together, their legs tangling. A wallpaper book shifted beneath them; Case shoved it roughly out of the way.

"Maddie," he groaned. "I want you. I want you so badly it's eating me alive."

Maddie couldn't fight him any longer. Couldn't fight herself. "I want you, too," she murmured, reaching for the top button of his shirt. "Now."

He stiffened, then crushed her against him. "Thank God," he muttered, and then kissed her again until the room seemed to spin wildly around her.

They removed their clothing hastily, heedlessly, leaving the garments in tangled heaps around them. Feverishly, they tumbled into each other's arms, and Maddie cried out with the pleasure of finally feeling his full length against her. It was even better than she had fantasized, she thought dazedly. All those months of wanting him, dreaming of him—loving him.

The words made her stiffen, though they'd sounded only inside her head. Case chose that moment to press his open mouth to her breast. She melted in reaction, all her misgivings evaporating in the heat of her response to him.

He moved against her, and she shifted to cradle him. And then she opened her eyes wide and pressed her hands to his chest. "Case, wait. We can't."

He moaned, and she felt a shudder of protest go through him. "God, Maddie, not now."

"I haven't changed my mind," she assured him quickly, suspecting she would suffer as greatly as he if they stopped now. But— "I'm not protected," she said. "Do you have anything?"

He grimaced. "Yeah," he admitted.

"Well?" she prodded impatiently when he hesitated. Relieved that he was more prepared for this than she had been, she was now eager to continue. He had already made her feel so much, given her more than she'd ever thought possible. She was anxious to learn how much more there could be for them.

Case sighed, his expression rueful. "I'll get it," he muttered, and he rolled away from her and reached for his duffel bag.

Something in his voice made her raise onto one elbow and stare at him. "You'd already thought of it," she said accusingly. "You weren't going to do anything about it, were you?"

"Maddie," he said, coming back to her. "You know damn well I want to have a family with you. Soon. But if you want to wait to have a baby, we'll wait."

She pressed a hand to her forehead, hardly able to believe she'd done it again. Case had simply assumed that her willingness to make love with him now meant everything was decided between them, that she would make no further resistance to his extensive plans. Oh, the arrogance of this man!

"Yes," she said firmly, "I most definitely want to wait to have a baby. Honestly, Case, you—"

He pushed her gently back down to the carpet, following her smoothly. "Later," he suggested, his hand sliding between them.

She caught her breath. "If you think you can seduce me until I . . ."

His fingers slipped lower. His lips moved softly, persuasively, against hers. "Yes?" he prompted, when her voice trailed away.

She moaned and wrapped her arms around his neck. "Later," she promised gruffly.

"Much later," he whispered, and kissed her as he plunged deeply, smoothly inside her.

Incapable of saying more than his name, Maddie forgot her fears about their future and abandoned herself to the joyous pleasures of the present.

"WHAT DO YOU THINK about this beige carpet, honey? The one called champagne. I like it."

"Case," Maddie said, struggling to rebutton her jeans beneath her hastily donned T-shirt. "Nothing has been decided."

Wearing only his jeans, which he hadn't even bothered to button, he set the carpet sample aside and reached for another. "I know. But that's my favorite so far."

Maddie sighed loudly. "I'm not talking about carpet."

"Well, we haven't even started choosing wallpaper."

She threw up her hands in frustration. "This is no time for wisecracks!" she snapped. "I want to talk about what happened here this afternoon."

Case glanced from her to the bits of clothing still scattered around them. A large brown splotch on the too-orange carpet marked the spot where they'd knocked over a soda can. Neither had even noticed the spill until much later. Case had shrugged it off, saying he was planning on replacing the carpet, anyway—even though this one certainly had its advantages.

Maddie had blushed crimson at the unmistakable double entendre. She'd been trying ever since to get him to be serious. And she was having absolutely no luck.

Case sighed at her expression and pushed away the samples. "All right, Maddie. Say whatever you want to say."

She didn't like the weary indulgence in his tone. She planted her hands on her hips and faced him determinedly. "Just because we—we—"

"Made love," he supplied helpfully.

She swallowed. "Just because we made love—" Oh, heavens, that seemed so solemn. So...so binding. "Just because we had sex," she said, but that sounded worse. She stumbled on without giving him a chance to voice the disapproval she saw in his expression. "I don't want you to think I've changed my mind about us. Nothing has changed."

"You're wrong, you know," he said almost conversationally. "A great deal has changed."

"I'm trying to say that we are *not* engaged," she snapped, nerves fraying.

He studied her face for a moment, then nodded. "All right. So what do you think about the champagne carpet?"

Maddie was tempted to scream. "You aren't even listening to me, are you?"

"I heard every word you said. We aren't engaged. But I still need carpet."

Suspiciously, she eyed him. He was making this much too easy. And perversely, his ready acceptance irked her. Wasn't he even going to argue with her? Was he that certain he could change her mind—or had he changed his? And, if so, why? She'd found their lovemaking the most spectacular, the most incredible experience of her entire life—but what if Case hadn't felt the same way?

Annoyed at her own anguished contradictions, she decided to follow his lead. She really didn't want to talk about this now, anyway. Carpet and wallpaper seemed so much safer.

SOMEHOW, she managed to concentrate on decorating decisions for the next couple of hours—but it wasn't easy. Every time they bent closely together over a page in the wallpaper book, every time their fingers brushed as they sorted through the carpet samples, every time Case followed her into a room and stood close beside her to discuss colors and options, Maddie was assailed by memories of their lovemaking. Of tangled limbs and sweat-sheened skin, of deep, hungry kisses and shudders of pleasure. Each time the memories surfaced, she pushed them determinedly away—but each time it was more difficult to do so.

She found herself in the master suite late that afternoon. It was an especially beautiful room, with a fireplace, deep crown molding, sliding glass doors leading to the covered porch at the back of the house, an attached sitting room with French doors opening onto a small, railed veranda at the front of the house, a dressing room, two huge walk-in closets, a built-in vanity with three-way mirror, a shower and a spa tub that would easily hold three people, should one have such inclinations. The suite was larger than the entire apartment she'd rented when she'd finished business school.

She stood in the center of the empty bedroom, picturing an enormous four-poster bed, an antique fainting couch, a fire spreading a golden glow through the room . . .

"I think this is my favorite room in the house," Case said from behind her, and Maddie was almost afraid he'd somehow seen the pictures in her head.

"It is nice," she said brusquely, keeping her face averted. "Did you want to stay with the same color scheme in here? The green and burgundy you want everywhere else?"

"What would you do in here—if this was to be your room?"

"Lace," she murmured, already seeing it. "Lots of lace. Softer colors than you've used elsewhere. Rose. Cream."

Firelight on lace. Glistening bodies stretched on satin. Candles flickering on a nightstand. Maddie almost groaned as her knees went liquid in response to the erotic images.

"Sounds nice," Case said, his voice rough, as though he was dealing with disturbing ideas of his own.

She turned abruptly, only to find him standing closer than she'd realized. So close they were almost touching.

Case reached out as though to steady her. His hands remained on her shoulders even after it was clear she wouldn't stumble. "Maddie," he murmured, his gaze focused on her mouth. "It seems like hours since I've kissed you."

"It has been hours," she whispered, already straining toward him.

"Then it's no wonder I'm starving for you again." He kissed her as though he were, indeed, starving, and she the only nourishment he craved. And Maddie kissed him back the same way. Because she simply couldn't resist him when he came to her like this.

A long time later, Case lifted his head. His eyes glittered like tempered steel when they locked with hers. "Making love with you was the greatest thing that ever happened to me," he said, suddenly fierce. "But it wasn't enough, Maddie. Don't you know it could never be enough?"

And he kissed her again, the embrace rough, demanding and yet strangely vulnerable.

So much had been left unsaid, so many things undecided. And yet Maddie felt something flicker to life deep inside her. It might have been hope. Or it might have been fear. But it felt more like an unnerving and yet exhilarating combination of both.

10

THE TOWN OF Mitchell's Fork always held a big festival on the Monday commemorating Independence Day. The festival began with a parade down Main Street, ending at the county fairgrounds, where rides and games, food and crafts booths and several entertainment stages awaited the crowds that always turned out. Beauty pageants, talent shows, sack races, tug-of-war, softball games, fireworks—the organizers billed the event as offering "something for everyone."

Children dashed through the fairgrounds, some followed by parents trying to keep them under control, others simply released for the afternoon with hopeful warnings to stay out of trouble. Two or three uniformed officers patrolled the grounds, occasionally reprimanding the rowdier of the youngsters, leading away the few revelers who'd imbibed too many "holiday spirits," watching for the few pickpockets and bullies who tried to spoil every gathering of honest citizens. But, on the whole, the event was relaxed and friendly, a chance for the hardworking people of the area to play and mingle for a day.

Maddie had been attending the festival with her family for as far back as she could remember. This year, there was only one major difference. This year, she knew she would see Case there.

Mike and Maddie settled Aunt Nettie and Grampa in comfortable lawn chairs in a well-shaded corner of the park, close enough to see the excitement, but away from the chaos of the midway area. The older relatives wouldn't stay long; Frank had come along in a separate vehicle to see them home when they tired. Mike and Maddie planned to stay longer, for personal reasons. Mike had been dating a widowed schoolteacher, who was supervising the teen talent show this year. And Maddie fully expected to spend at least part of the day with Case.

"Are you sure I can't get you anything else, Grampa?" she asked when everyone had been settled. Her grandfather, still frail but mostly recovered from his attack a few weeks earlier, held a paper cup of lemonade in one hand and an ice-cream cone in the other. He wasn't usually allowed many sweets, but on an occasion like this, diets tended to be forgotten.

Grampa shook his head. "You run along and find your friends now," he told her. "Have fun."

"Stay off that roller coaster," Aunt Nettie admonished, looking up from the pineapple sherbet she'd been devouring with delicate greed. "You know I don't trust those flimsy rides, especially when I know how fast those disreputable-looking carnies threw them together."

Maddie grinned. Aunt Nettie had been saying the same words to her every year since she was in elementary school—and Maddie answered exactly as she always had. "I won't go on the roller coaster, Aunt Nettie."

She'd never mentioned that she hated roller coasters and wouldn't have ridden one if she'd been guaranteed a safe ride by Saint Peter, himself. Aunt Nettie seemed to get such satisfaction from believing that Maddie stayed away from them only out of respectful obedience to her wise and watchful great-aunt.

"Maddie. There you are, we've been looking for you." Jill rushed up with a beaming smile, followed more slowly by Jackson. Wearing a brightly colored knit shorts outfit, and with her dark hair pulled into a ponytail, Jill looked little older than she had when she and Maddie had attended the festival as giggly teenagers. She seemed just as eager now to plunge into the activities.

"You go have fun with your friends," Frank told Maddie, waving a beefy arm toward the activities. "I'll take good care of the folks."

Maddie smiled gratefully at him. "I know you will, Frank. Thank you."

His cheeks pinkened a bit at the heartfelt praise. He waved her off in embarrassment.

Maddie kissed her father's cheek. "I'm going with Jill and Jackson now."

"All right. You stay out of trouble, you hear?"

Maddie giggled. "I am almost thirty, you know," she reminded him.

"Yes, but until that so-called fiancé gets some control over you, it looks like I'm still responsible for you," Mike teased.

Maddie punched his arm. "We'll talk about your archaic sexism—and your weird sense of humor—later," she warned him. "And it won't be pretty."

Mike made a conspicuous show of gulping.

"Come on, Maddie, there's a magician starting a show on the east stage in fifteen minutes. I've heard he's pretty good," Jill urged.

"And the Optimists Club has a barbecue booth again this year," Jackson added, licking his lips in anticipation. "I want a barbecued pork sandwich with extra spicy sauce and coleslaw."

Laughing, Maddie allowed herself to be pulled into the midst of the festival. But even as she chatted with her friends, she found herself constantly scanning the crowd for one lean, dark-haired, gray-eyed man.

CASE SPOTTED Maddie soon after he arrived at the fairgrounds. She looked sexy as hell in a navy-and-white sailor-collared pullover and brief navy shorts. He scowled when he noted that she was clinging to Jackson Babbit's arm.

He thought he had made it clear to Babbit that Maddie was already taken.

And then his scowl eased when he saw Jill Parsons hanging on to Babbit's other arm. The three of them were laughing as comfortably together as a trio of teenage buddies as they watched a determined boy trying to dunk the junior high principal into a tank of water by hitting a target with a softball.

One guy, two girls. Nothing fair about that, he decided with a smirk. He promptly invited himself to join them.

A hand fell onto her shoulder, and Maddie somehow knew who it was even before she turned her head. Her pulse leapt in anticipation.

She glanced up through her lashes. Case smiled down at her, and the expression in his silvery gray eyes made her tremble. She knew exactly what he was thinking, because she was thinking it, too. They were both remembering their dinner date the night before, which had ended on the newly laid champagne carpet in his still-empty den.

At least they hadn't spilled any soft drinks that time, Maddie thought ruefully. That had only happened the first time, two weeks ago. Though she'd told herself she wasn't going to make love with him again, at least until she'd come to some decision about their future, she'd been unable to resist when he'd turned to take her in his arms. They'd made love on two other occasions—and both times were as spectacular as the first. She was afraid she was growing addicted to Case's lovemaking—an addiction she didn't want to overcome.

"Hi," Case murmured, his gaze caressing her mouth in lieu of a kiss.

"Hi," she said, pushing the syllable past the tightness in her throat. Oh, he looked wonderful today. His dark hair fell in the characteristic tumble on his forehead, making her itch to brush it back, and he wore a close-fitting white knit shirt and his favorite low-slung jeans. He'd gained a few pounds in the weeks since he'd arrived in town, so that he looked healthy and fit again. The limp was almost gone now, though the scars would always remain. It was all Maddie could do not to throw herself on him right there in front of the entire population of Mitchell's Fork.

"Earth to Maddie, come in, Maddie," Jill said, her voice bubbling with amusement.

Maddie flushed, wondering how long she'd stood there staring at Case. She hastily dropped Jackson's arm and stepped away from both men, needing a moment to collect herself.

"Did you just get here, Case?" Jill asked.

He dragged his gaze away from Maddie's face to look at her friend. "Yeah. Have I missed anything exciting?"

"Only the Junior Miss Mitchell's Fork finals. Alison Derryberry won. Lucy Stickling expected her daughter, Nicole, to win this year and she really showed her butt, as my grandmother would say. Claimed Patty Anne Derryberry bribed the judges to let her daughter win. That's ridiculous, of course. If the judges could be bribed, Casey Cooper would have won—that's Major Cooper's daughter, in case you didn't figure that out. Danny the delinquent's sister."

Case blinked and Maddie knew he was trying without much success to follow Jill's tale. Maddie took pity on him. "Never mind," she said. "That's all just silly gossip. What would you like to do now that you're here?"

"Why don't you show me around?" he suggested, slipping an arm around her waist. He gave Jackson a bland, faintly challenging smile. "We'll make it a foursome, shall we?"

Jackson grinned. "I thought my luck was too good to last at having these two lovely ladies all to myself." He turned to Jill with a flourish. "Well, darlin'? Want to be my date for the rest of the festival?"

Jill rolled her eyes and sighed deeply. "Lacking any better offers, I suppose I must accept."

Jackson groaned and slapped a hand to the embroidered chest of his white Western-cut shirt. "You wound me deeply," he accused her. "But to be honored with your presence for even this short time, I will gladly suffer the edge of your tongue."

He managed to inject just enough innuendo into the words to make Jill blush rosily and slap his hand. And then she haughtily declared that she wanted something to drink and swept him off to a refreshment booth, leaving Maddie and Case to follow at a more leisurely pace.

"Those two squabble like cats and dogs, don't they?" Case observed, nodding toward Jill and Jackson.

Maddie smiled. "Always have. Well, almost always. They dated for a while in high school, actually."

"You're kidding."

"No. It was Jackson's senior year, and Jill was a sophomore. They seemed to be crazy about each other, but then they broke up when Jill caught Jackson making out with Linda Prince behind the gym. They didn't speak for years. Jackson and Linda were married a couple of years later, but it didn't last long. When they divorced, Jill was married to a guy she'd met through the bank. Then Jackson married someone else—another disaster, I'm afraid."

"And now both Jill and Jackson are single."

"Right. Jill claims she wouldn't date Jackson again if he were the only single man in the state of Mississippi—she doesn't trust him as far as she could throw him. But lately they've been spending a lot of time together, mostly because he *is* just about the only single man her age in Mitchell's Fork."

"Think they'll make a match of it?"

Maddie shrugged. "Either that, or they'll end up hating each other again. Who knows?"

"You're staying out of it, right?"

"Far out of it," she assured him. "There's no quicker way to lose a friend—or two friends—than to get involved in their love life."

"Wise observation. Personally, the only way I'd get involved in Babbit's love life is if he made some misguided effort to include you in it. I'm afraid I'd have to get involved then. Strongly involved."

Maddie looked at him suspiciously. "Why does that sound like a threat?"

Case managed to look dangerous and innocent all at the same time. "I can't imagine."

It didn't take long for Case to get into the spirit of the Independence Day festival. He and Jackson started a more or less friendly rivalry over the carnival games, challenging each other at breaking balloons with darts, throwing basketballs into bushel baskets, tossing footballs through hanging tires and dunking the school principal, who took one look at the two men approaching with such determination and promptly resigned his seat in the booth. Both Maddie and Jill were loaded down with prizes before the afternoon was over. When her arms got too full to allow her to participate, Maddie stuffed them into the trunk of her car.

"Let's go on some rides," Jill suggested when the guys declared a draw to their macho-flexing competition.

"Anything but the roller coaster," Maddie agreed with a laugh, then had to explain her Aunt Nettie's traditional warning to Case.

He grinned. "I don't suppose you'd dare disobey her."

"Are you kidding? She'd send me to my room for a week."

Case nodded sympathetically. "She'd probably ground *me* for encouraging you. To tell you the truth, Maddie, your great-aunt is the only member of your family who terrifies me."

"And justifiably so," she assured him with a laugh.

They passed a crepe-strung dais on their way to the midway. Three men stood to one side of it, watching the activities around them with obvious condescending indulgence. Case made a sound of distaste. "I suppose your sorry excuse for a sheriff thinks he's keeping law and order at the festival?" he asked, nodding toward the uniformed man.

Maddie grimaced. "Of course he does."

"I don't suppose he or any of the others have noticed the three delinquents who've been running all over the park on four-wheelers." He'd commented more than once how dangerous it was for Danny Cooper and his buddies to have the ATVs in the crowded fairgrounds, and the others had agreed, though Maddie had pointed out that at least the boys were staying on the outside of the crowd, riding their vehicles along the outer fences.

"Trust me," Jackson muttered. "They've noticed. But you don't really think they're going to throw the Cooper kid out of the festival, do you? His daddy sponsored most of the activities here today."

Case grunted his disdain, then looked back toward Sheriff McAdams. "Who are the two pompous-looking guys with him?"

"They don't just look pompous, they are," Jill said fervently, overhearing the question. "That's Mayor Sloane and Major Cooper."

"So that's Major Cooper," Case murmured, eyeing the man Jill had pointed out. "The man who owns half the town, hmm?"

"Only a third or so," Jackson murmured, though he looked uncomfortable. Maddie knew that Jackson, like most of the other local businessmen, tended to tread carefully around the mayor and his buddy.

"What branch of the service was he in?"

Jill giggled. "None, Case. Major is his first name, not his rank."

Three teenage boys stepped into their path, their four-wheelers abandoned for a while. Maddie almost groaned. *Great,* she thought. *Now Case can get into a brawl with them right here in front of their ever-lovin' daddies.*

Case seemed determined to ignore Danny and his pals. He wrapped an arm around Maddie's shoulders and pointed toward the slowly turning Ferris wheel. "Want to take a spin?" he asked her.

"Well, if it ain't the spy guy," Danny drawled before Maddie could answer. "Hey, Brannigan. Hear you traded your fancy Ferrari for a Jeep Grand Cherokee."

Case paused, then looked over his shoulder. "Yeah," he said. "Of course, I didn't get as much as I should have for the Ferrari. It had some damage to the paint job."

"Ain't that a shame," Danny commiserated with a cocky grin. His buddies snickered.

"Beat the crap out of 'em, Case," Jill whispered.

"Jill! Stop it!" Maddie chided, though she knew Jill was only kidding to try to break the tension around them.

"Hope nothing happens to your new wheels," Danny said, challenging Case with his eyes.

"Someone will definitely pay this time if it does," Case answered flatly.

Danny cocked his head. "'S that right?"

"You can bet your front teeth on it." Case sounded—and looked—so dangerous that Maddie swallowed. Both Jackson and Jill were looking at him in sudden surprise, and the few onlookers nearby blinked at the menace in the newcomer's voice. Only an idiot, Maddie thought, would confront Case Brannigan when he looked like this.

"What's going on here?" Sheriff McAdams demanded as he ambled toward them, his flabby belly pushed belligerently over his belt. Close by, Mayor Sloane and Major Cooper watched intently, scowling at the man who'd had the nerve to threaten their boys.

"Brannigan, you ain't harassing these boys, are you? I told you, you got no cause to accuse them of messing with your car. You got no witnesses, no evidence, nothing. Now I'm telling you to leave them alone, you hear?"

Maddie gasped indignantly. "Case was not harassing these boys," she protested. "Danny's the one who was doing all the talking. Case just—"

Case's arm tightened around her shoulders. "I do my own talking," he muttered.

"We don't want any trouble, Sheriff," Jackson said quickly. "We were just enjoying the festival."

McAdams struck a practiced, weary-lawman pose that made Maddie ill. "You'd think a bunch of adults would have something better to do with their time than to play at the fair, but that's your business, I suppose. Get along with you and don't give me any more trouble."

Case stood there for a moment, his eyes locked with the sheriff's just long enough to make the other man start to look nervous. And then Case deliberately turned his back on the older man. "Let's go," he said, taking Maddie's hand.

None of them looked back.

"Oh, man, Brannigan," Jackson groaned as soon as they'd disappeared into the crowd. "You sure know how to win friends and influence people."

"Well, *I* think he deserves applause," Jill defended Case spiritedly. "Danny Cooper needs to be taken behind someone's woodshed, and McAdams is a stupid, pompous jackass. Case doesn't have to kiss up to either of them."

Jackson flushed uncomfortably. "Yeah, well, he doesn't have a business to run here," he muttered. "He can pick up and leave at any time. Do I have to remind you that Cooper's the biggest customer of your bank? You think Peacock won't fire your butt in a minute if Cooper orders him to?"

"He'd better not try it!" Jill said, but she suddenly looked a bit wary.

Case shook his head. "This quarrel is between them and me," he assured her. "Neither of you need to get involved."

"It's getting ridiculous," Maddie said, though a cold lump had settled in her stomach with Jackson's words. *He can pick up and leave at any time,* he'd said. Was it only an example—or an accurate prediction?

Ignoring the unpleasant question, she frowned at Case. "You're too old to be feuding with a teenager," she accused him. "And there's no reason for you to get involved in a battle with McAdams. You should simply stay away from all of them. That's what most of us around here do."

"Undisciplined teenagers become adult criminals. And how can you ignore your own town leaders? What happens when you need police protection? Or input into your town government?" he demanded.

She shrugged. "We've managed to get by so far."

He shook his head in disgust. "That doesn't mean I have to like it."

"I didn't say you had to like it," she reminded him primly. "Just accept it."

He didn't look at all convinced.

Maddie couldn't help worrying.

THERE WAS A DANCE that evening. A country band provided music from a stage, while a hard-packed dirt arena served as a dance floor. "I've never danced outside before," Case said as he swung Maddie around in a lively two-step to a song made famous by George Strait.

She smiled and spun easily in his arms. "You catch on quickly," she complimented him.

He grinned. "Thank you right kindly, ma'am."

She groaned. "Don't try to talk with a Southern accent, Case. Trust me, it just doesn't work for you."

He laughed. "Whatever you say, Maddie."

He said that a lot, she mused, swinging around him again. The funny thing was, she was starting to like it.

They sat out the next number, sharing a picnic table with Jackson and Jill, Maddie's cousin, Lisa, her frequent escort, Charlie Campbell and Lisa's teenagers, Jeff and Kathy. Case chatted easily with the others, making an obvious effort to fit in and be accepted.

Maddie noticed that he didn't seem to mind all the questions he was asked. He explained repeatedly that he had worked in law enforcement for a time, but had recently retired, that he was thinking of starting an investment-counseling business, and that, yes, he was remodeling the Fielding place and planned to settle permanently in Mitchell's Fork. Each time he said that, everyone looked speculatively at Maddie. It happened so often, it finally stopped bothering her. Let them speculate, she thought. She didn't owe anyone explanations.

Jeff sat directly across the table from Case, and it was obvious that he thought of Case as a hero. Maddie thought she understood why. Jeff's own father had walked out on them when Jeff was very small and hadn't made contact since. Jeff wasn't too crazy about his mother's new boyfriend, whom Maddie thought of as pleasant, but a bit lazy and irresponsible.

Case, on the other hand, was a former DEA agent who'd been shot in the line of duty, an exciting, adventurous man who'd driven into town in a flashy sports car and purchased one of the biggest houses in the area.

A man who'd come to town to "claim his woman"—an objective Jeff must have found dashing and romantic. Not only that, Case had taken on the bullies who'd been making Jeff's school life so miserable. How could he not see Case as a hero?

It was getting harder all the time for Maddie not to think of him in much the same way, though Case's stubborn streak was causing her some concern at the moment. She couldn't help worrying that he was getting into a situation that could only end unpleasantly.

Several townspeople stopped by the table to surreptitiously congratulate Case on standing up to the sheriff—or to warn him not to do so again.

"You're stirring up a hornet's nest, boy," Hank the barber muttered in Case's ear, Maddie being the only one close enough to overhear. "You don't want to go messin' with Cooper and his men."

Case only thanked the man for his warning and promised to be in the next week for a haircut.

"You aren't listening to anyone, are you?" Maddie complained.

He smiled and leaned over to brush his lips across hers. "I'm listening," he assured her. "Stop worrying about it."

Innocuous as it had been, Maddie knew that light kiss had been seen and noted by several very interested observers. She cleared her throat and gulped the last sip of her cola.

The band went into a toe-tapping country-swing number and Jackson pulled Jill onto the dance floor. Maddie watched them, then chuckled when she saw her father and his schoolteacher friend doing a lively jig across the dance floor. She pointed them out to Lisa.

"They're such a cute couple," Lisa said with a smile. "Think you're going to end up with a stepmother, Maddie?"

"I wouldn't mind if I did," she answered, knowing Case was listening with interest. "Mona's a nice woman and Dad's been alone a long time. She makes him happy."

Case squeezed Maddie's hand beneath the table, apparently in approval of her answer.

Lisa suddenly frowned. "Look who's dancing beside them," she muttered. "Mayor Sloane and his wife. That guy dances like he's got a corncob up his butt, doesn't he?"

Case laughed. Maddie sighed. "You've been spending too much time with Aunt Nettie again," she accused her cousin, though she couldn't help smiling a little. The mayor *was* a self-consciously stiff dancer. She knew he was only out there to make sure everyone could compliment him on fully participating in the town festival.

A flashbulb lit next to him, and Maddie shook her head when she identified the photographer as one of the two full-time reporters from the *Mitchell's Fork Weekly News*. She knew whose picture she'd find on the front page next week. Of course, the mayor managed to get his picture on that front page *every* week. Usually shaking hands with Major Cooper or accepting a donation for some charity or another from him.

At least Danny and his buddies weren't making trouble at the dance, she thought optimistically. She could hear the faint whine of their ATVs and the occasional *crack-crack-crack* of firecrackers. Heaven only knew what they were up to, but that wasn't her problem—or Case's, thank goodness.

"I think I'll have another lemonade," Case said, pushing himself to his feet. "You want anything, Maddie?"

"Lemonade sounds good," she said, shoving aside the empty cup that had held watery cola.

"Anyone else?" Case asked politely.

"I'll go with you, Case," Jeff offered eagerly, jumping to his feet. "I want another hot dog."

"Another one?" Case teased. "Where are you putting them, boy?"

"He has a hollow leg," Lisa answered resignedly. "Two of them, actually. There's just no filling him up."

Charlie excused himself to go talk to someone he knew across the arena, leaving only Maddie, Jill, Lisa and Kathy at the table for a brief time.

The men were hardly out of hearing before Lisa turned to Maddie with a demanding question. "Well?" she said. "What's going on with you and Case? Are you officially engaged, or what?"

Maddie made a face at her cousin's nosiness. "Neither officially nor unofficially," she answered. "We're only dating."

"C'mon, Maddie, I've seen the way the two of you look at each other. He's crazy about you—and don't try to tell me you don't feel the same way about him. What in the world are you waiting for?"

"He's a very nice man, Maddie," Kathy said with a romantic-teenager sigh. "What *are* you waiting for?"

She didn't know how to answer them. How could she explain that she was waiting for Case to tell her he loved her? To convince her that he valued her for herself, and not for what she represented?

How did she tell them that she lay in bed every night longing for him, and yet terrified that he would break her heart again? Her fears that he would soon grow tired of playing house and be off again in search of adventure, leaving her behind.

Even his defiance of Cooper and his cronies worried her. Maybe Case wasn't worried about them because he didn't really intend to stay in Mitchell's Fork long enough for them to give him any trouble. Silly of her to think that, of course, particularly since he was working so hard on remodeling the house he said he wanted to make his permanent home. But still, she worried. And she waited.

She shrugged helplessly. "You wouldn't understand," she assured Lisa and Kathy.

Lisa looked at her perceptively. "Maybe I do," she said slowly. "He's . . . different from the other men around here, isn't he?"

"Yes," Maddie murmured, glancing at the refreshment booth where Case stood in line with giggling teenagers and soft-middled businessmen, young men in baseball caps and jeans, young mothers with small children clinging to their hands. He looked so lean and hard and dangerous among the ordinary citizens of Mitchell's Fork, Mississippi. How could he, or anyone, believe he'd ever fit in?

Maddie didn't even know if she wanted to believe it, herself. She'd fallen for the dashing, adventurous man she'd met in Cancún, the man who'd introduced her to passion and excitement and a whole world of possibilities. Did she really want him to change, to be like the other men here? Hadn't she already come to the conclusion that she wanted more out of life than she could find within the limited boundaries of Mitchell's Fork?

Case was already on his way back to her, a paper cup in each hand. Seeing her watching him, he smiled. A dangerous, reckless, adventurer's smile.

Yes, she thought with a shiver. Case wasn't like any other man she'd ever known.

He slipped onto the bench beside her and pressed his thigh tightly to hers. She felt the heat building inside her, and knew it was reflected in the blush on her cheeks. Hoping to conceal her reactions from her openly interested cousin, she cleared her throat and tried to think of something to say. "There will be fireworks a little later this evening."

Case gave her another wicked smile. "I certainly hope so," he murmured.

Lisa giggled.

Maddie's cheeks flamed.

The band started playing a crooning country ballad. Couples melded into each other's arms, dancing beneath the stars, their backdrop the glittering lights and cheery decorations of the festival. Case stood and held out a hand to Maddie. "Dance with me," he said.

She placed her hand in his and allowed him to lead her onto the packed-dirt dance floor. He took her into his arms and the noise and the crowd fell away, leaving Maddie aware of only Case and the music, and the heat that slowly built between them as they swayed gently, hardly moving.

"It's been a great day, Maddie," Case murmured into her ear. "I like your town, your festival, your friends. And I love—"

Whatever he would have said—and she'd held her breath in anticipation—was interrupted by a loud, splintering crash, followed by a chorus of horrified screams.

Case stiffened, and then he was gone, dashing in the direction of the noise, leaving Maddie to follow, her head spinning from the abrupt change in mood.

11

SEVERAL OLD WOODEN bleachers ringed the main arena of the fairgrounds. A few people had already begun to gather there to view the fireworks display scheduled to begin at 9:00 p.m.—still twenty minutes away.

Maddie was horrified to see that one of the larger bleachers had collapsed in the center, and the remainder of the structure was teetering dangerously. Five children—looking to be between seven and twelve years old—were perched at the top, clinging to the swaying wooden railings and screaming.

Several of the benches below them had fallen, leaving the children balanced precariously on the top seat, some fifteen feet above the ground, a gaping dark hole below them. The sun was setting, and the scene was illuminated only by the glaring arena lights overhead, casting long shadows over the crowd and adding to the terrifying sense of looming disaster.

"Oh, my God," Maddie whispered, standing very still as she pictured the rest of that structure falling, landing in a jumbled pile of debris and children.

There was pandemonium around her—people running, shouting, screaming. No one seemed to be in charge, though McAdams and his deputy were scurrying among the others, looking panicky and indecisive.

The situation quickly changed.

"You!" Case shouted to a group of strong-looking teenage boys—one of them Jeff. "Brace the supports!"

The boys took only a moment to catch his meaning. And then they circled the swaying supports of the bleacher, grabbing hold and straining to hold them upright. Several other men and women rushed to help them. Coming out of her temporary paralysis, Maddie threw herself into the group around an outer support, planting her feet and holding the wooden leg with both hands. Though there were six other people surrounding the same support, she felt the wood swaying and she knew they wouldn't be able to hold it for long.

Hearing something above her, she looked up at the children. One of them, a boy of about ten, moved as though to climb down once the adults were in place beneath him. "No!" Case yelled, making the child freeze in automatic reaction to the deep voice of authority. "Stay put," Case shouted to the boy. "I'm coming after you."

Maddie swallowed an automatic cry of protest. Case was going up? What if he fell? What if he brought down the structure with him, children and all? Shouldn't he wait until someone arrived with a ladder?

The bleacher groaned and shifted. Maddie and the people around her frantically shuffled closer, throwing their weight against the wooden legs, trying to serve as human beams.

"It's all going to come down!" McAdams yelled from somewhere behind Maddie. "Everybody clear out of here."

A woman screamed. Maddie recognized her as the mother of one of the children stranded at the top. Glaring over her shoulder at the ineffectual and tactless sheriff, Maddie spoke to the horrified woman standing behind her, looking tearfully up at the children. "It's all right, Carol," she called over the noise. "Case will get them down."

For some reason, that seemed to reassure the woman almost as much as it did Maddie.

Jackson and Mike appeared suddenly beside Case, who'd been checking each support, making sure the volunteers were in place to provide the most strength. After a hurried consultation, Jackson, Mike and two other men boosted Case upward. He caught hold of a horizontal support and tested his weight against it. The wood groaned.

Maddie caught her breath. Her arms were beginning to tremble as the wood swayed against her. She braced her feet more solidly into the dirt and trampled grass beneath them.

Very slowly, while Maddie craned her neck upward to watch, Case made his way toward the top, testing each board before placing his weight. Around Maddie, the crowd, which had been shouting suggestions and instructions, had fallen silent, as though afraid loud noise would adversely affect the outcome of the tense drama taking place above them.

"Get that man down from there," McAdams suddenly yelled, his voice loud and strident in the silence. "He's going to bring it all down. We'll wait for the rescue team."

"This bleacher isn't going to hold long enough for the team to get here," someone snapped at the sheriff. "Brannigan's doing all he knows to do."

Case had almost reached the top. Maddie kept thinking of his weak leg. Would it hold him? What if...?

She gasped when a board broke beneath him. It fell, landing two feet from where Maddie stood. She flinched in automatic reaction, then forced herself to remain still, knowing that only she and the others around her were keeping the whole bleacher section from falling over.

Case snatched at the seat on which the children waited for him, and a moment later, he had safely joined them. Maddie released a long shaky breath, dimly aware that the spectators around her did the same.

Case had his hands full, balancing up on that narrow bench with five children clinging to him in panic. Maddie noticed how calm and gentle he was with them, soothing their fears even as the splintered wood strained beneath them.

"How will he get them down?" the frantic mother behind Maddie moaned. "Oh, I should never have let Bobby play up there with the other kids. I should have made him stay with me."

"You didn't know this would happen," Maddie murmured reassuringly. Why hadn't anyone noticed how rickety the old bleachers had become? Why hadn't something been done to ensure safety before the festival?

"Oh, God, what's he doing now?" the woman asked in a whisper.

Maddie looked upward as Case leaned over the railing and shouted something to Jackson. Jackson promptly climbed onto the shoulders of burly truck driver Andy Smith, a bearded, former high school football star who was a frequent customer in Maddie's restaurant. Two other men moved to support Jackson's legs as he stretched upward.

Case turned to ten-year-old Bobby, and motioned him forward. Wide-eyed in the artificial lighting, Bobby shook his head.

Maddie watched as Case smiled and urged the boy to him. Moving slowly, painstakingly carefully, Case held the boy around the waist and lowered him to Jackson's waiting arms. Half a dozen other people were waiting to take the child from Jackson.

"Oh, thank God," Carol gasped when her son was safely on the ground. She ran toward him.

Sirens were wailing in the background now. Dividing her attention between the action above her and the chaos around her, Maddie noticed for the first time that someone lay on the ground near where the center section had collapsed, and that some people were grouped in that area. She still didn't understand what had happened.

One by one, Case lowered the next three children to Jackson, two small boys and then an older girl. Finally, he was left on the bleachers with the last child, a small, crying girl who'd been clinging to his leg since he'd joined her. He turned to lift her. She shook her head and buried her face in his shoulder, obviously afraid to be lowered over the side.

"C'mon, Polly, let the man get you down," someone yelled.

"That's right, sweetie, help him out now," a woman cried, her voice quavering.

Polly shook her head and burrowed more deeply into Case's arms.

Something snapped loudly beneath the bleachers. People screamed and shouted as another section collapsed. The ones who'd been standing beneath that section scattered, just missing being hit by falling wood and benches. Maddie flinched, but remained where she was, praying the section above her would hold.

Case and little Polly were roughly shaken, the wood swaying wildly beneath them as the human supporters threw everything they had into trying to hold the structure upright a little while longer. Case had the child gripped solidly in one arm as he clung to the railing, one leg dangling over the yawning abyss in front of his narrow seat.

Very slowly, Case eased the child over the side. Jackson was waiting. So were the child's shaken parents. The crowd broke into cheers.

The sound of wood splintering made itself heard above the noise. "It's coming down!" Case shouted, both legs dangling now as the bench he'd been on began to tilt sideways. "Everyone move away. Go! *Maddie!* Get out from under it!"

He was trying to keep anyone else from getting hurt, Maddie realized, staying where she was. Without thought to the danger he was in, he was trying to run off the people who were holding up the structure he was on so that none of them would be trapped beneath the bleachers when they came down.

A group of firemen were running toward the bleachers with a ladder. Maddie knew they wouldn't make it in time. She kept praying. Could Case survive a fall of that distance, trapped among lengths of wood and jutting nails?

On his feet again, Jackson leapt toward the bleachers, motioning the men around him to join him. "Brannigan!" he yelled. "Jump!"

Without hesitation, Case released the support he'd been clinging to and dropped. Jackson, Andy and several other men caught him in a classic fireman's hold just as the rescue team reached them.

The bleachers came down right behind him. Maddie threw herself out of the way, along with everyone else around her. She stumbled and fell, landing on top of someone else, but neither of them were hurt. The crash was almost deafening, followed by a heavy cloud of dust kicked up in the fall.

Shoving herself upright, Maddie threw herself into Case's arms, frantically checking to make sure he was in one piece. He seemed a bit shaky, but solid. "Oh, my God, you scared me half to death," she said, catching his shirt in both fists and glaring at him. "I can't believe you did that."

"Are you all right?" he asked, just as anxious as she. "You weren't hit by anything that fell?"

"I'm fine," she assured him.

He caught her against him for another hug.

Suddenly, they found themselves in the middle of a mob. Parents of the children tearfully thanked Case for his daring rescue. Others wanted to congratulate him on his quick thinking. The reporter from the *Mitchell's Fork Weekly* wanted to interview him on the spot. Someone pushed the man impatiently aside.

"What the hell is going on here?" McAdams demanded, pushing through the crowd, belatedly taking charge. "How did this happen?"

"It was Kale Sloane who done it," an adolescent boy insisted, shouting to be heard. "He was on his four-wheeler and he barreled into the bottom of the bleachers. The whole thing started coming down. Me and Curtis had to jump off. I skinned my knee."

Danny Cooper, who'd been standing beside his father on the outskirts of the crowd—both well out of range of any potential danger—stepped forward belligerently. "Kale didn't mean to run into the bleacher. He hit a slick patch of grass and lost control."

Maddie looked toward the medical technicians now bending over the body she'd seen on the ground earlier. She saw the ATV that lay on its side nearby, a pile of rubble half covering it. She spotted the mayor and his wife hovering over their son. "Is Kale all right?"

Someone nodded. "He's okay. Looks like he might have broken a leg, but it doesn't look serious. They're taking him to the emergency room now."

Anger seething in his narrowed eyes, Case turned on the sheriff. "Why the hell didn't you stop those kids from running around the fairgrounds on those things? I've known all day someone was going to get hurt if no one did anything about them."

McAdams didn't like being criticized in front of his constituents. "They weren't doing anything illegal," he insisted. "They were keeping the ATVs out of the crowd. The kid lost control. It was an accident."

"It was an accident waiting to happen," Case insisted. "Those bleachers have to be fifty years old. The wood's rotted, the supports were a joke. It's a wonder they haven't already fallen. As for the ATVs, only an idiot would be racing one through a fairground full of kids!"

Danny spat out something Maddie didn't quite catch. The look he gave Case contained pure hatred, an ugly emotion Maddie found deeply disturbing in a boy Danny's age.

His father scowled. "I was watching the boys," Cooper insisted. "I'd told 'em to stay away from the crowds, and they were. It was all an accident. We don't need an outsider coming in criticizing our way of doing things around here, do we?" he demanded, turning to the silent onlookers who were watching the confrontation.

To his displeasure, they remained silent.

Cooper scowled. "Let's go see about Kale, son," he said, turning to his sullen boy. "Everyone's just shaken up over what almost happened, that's all."

McAdams was still glaring at Case. "He's right, you know," he said more quietly, trying to sound menacing. "We don't need outsiders telling us what to do."

"I'm not an outsider," Case replied, sounding completely menacing without particularly trying. "I'm a property owner in this town, and I'll be a registered voter soon. You're an elected official, McAdams. If you can't handle the job, or the troublemakers in this town—no matter how much money or influence they have—then the voters just may have to find someone who can."

"That's telling him, Case!" someone called out of the crowd. Maddie recognized the voice as Jill's.

McAdams flushed and scowled. He turned to motion at the townspeople staring at him. "All right, clear out. We've got to let the emergency crews through."

"I guess the fireworks display is canceled," the boy who had skinned his knee grumbled.

Cooper had come back into view by then. "No, it's not," he said quickly. "I've paid to bring this town a spectacular exhibit for Independence Day and we're still going to have it. We'll call it a celebration that no one was seriously injured here today."

Some people applauded. Others drifted away.

"I think I've had all the excitement I can take for one evening," Case muttered.

"Me, too," Maddie agreed fervently.

"Want to get out of here?"

She nodded and slipped her still-shaking hand beneath his arm.

It took them over half an hour to leave the fairgrounds. It seemed that nearly everyone wanted to personally congratulate Case on his rescue. Maddie noticed that Jackson was getting a fair amount of attention, as well—and seemed to be enjoying every minute of it, unlike Case, who was looking more and more desperate to get out of the limelight.

Maddie took his hand. "Run," she whispered during a brief lull in the attention he was getting.

He lifted an eyebrow. "What?"

She was already tugging at his hand, pulling him toward the parking lot. "Run!"

Catching her meaning, he smiled and ran.

MADDIE SPRAWLED limply in the passenger seat of Case's new Grand Cherokee as he drove swiftly away from the fairgrounds. She noticed that he was heading in the direction of his house, rather than hers. She didn't protest.

"Still sure you want to make Mitchell's Fork your home, Case?" she asked, finding it hard to believe he was still clinging to his idealized vision of "normal life." "There's not usually this much excitement around here, but there will always be the gossip and the hypocrisy and the petty politics and everything else that comes along with a small, relatively poor town."

"Yes. But this is also the same town that welcomed me with friendly smiles and foil-covered casseroles, the town that turned out en masse when your grandfather was taken to the hospital, where the people have watched you grow up and rally around to protect you now. This is where I want to make my home, Maddie. With you."

She fell silent, unable to argue with his defense of her town, and reluctant to do so, anyway.

The brass porch lights were burning when Case pulled up in front of the house. Their golden glow lighted the front porch, a welcoming sight that warmed Maddie's heart. It looked like a home, she thought wistfully.

Even though she knew there was no furniture inside, that the bedrooms upstairs were all empty and quiet, she could so easily picture walking into this beautiful house and being welcomed home by a loving family. Was that what Case envisioned whenever he looked at the house he'd been working on so hard for the past few weeks? Did the image make him ache with the same hollow emptiness Maddie felt, the same deep, wordless longing?

Case killed the engine. "I could use a drink," he said.

"Me, too," she murmured, managing a weak smile.

He chuckled softly and caressed her cheek. "You don't drink," he reminded her.

"I'm thinking about starting."

He leaned over and brushed her lips with his. "I think I can offer something more relaxing and pleasurable than alcohol."

She lifted a hand to the side of his neck, feeling his pulse pounding rapidly beneath her fingertips. "I'm sure you can."

"Let's go in," he said, sounding suddenly impatient.

She reached for her door handle.

THEY STOOD in the center of the big, empty den, facing each other without speaking, the only light spilling in from the foyer beyond. Maddie's hands rested on Case's chest and his hands reached for her hips as they embraced with their eyes, saying so much without words.

Case brushed his lips across her forehead. Maddie closed her eyes, breathing in the spicy male scent of him. Already, her heart was pounding with excitement, her skin tingling in anticipation of his touch.

She'd once longed for adventure. Case Brannigan was proving to be all the adventure she'd ever imagined.

His hands shifted slowly behind her, cupping her bottom and drawing her closer against him. Slowly they came together, the heat from their bodies penetrating their T-shirts and jeans. Her eyes still closed, Maddie tilted her head upward. Case's mouth covered hers in immediate response to the silent invitation.

He was hard against her, his arousal unmistakable. Yet he seemed to be in no hurry. He took his time kissing her, using the tip of his tongue to trace every centimeter of her mouth—the slight dip at the top, the full curve of her lower lip, the shallow dimples in the corners. Only then did he delve between her lips to taste her more deeply.

Maddie's murmur of desire was lost inside his mouth. She slid her arms around his neck, holding him more tightly to her. He was so strong, so solid. So real. Unlike the fantasy lover who'd danced just outside of her reach for those six lonely months after Cancún.

Case said something incoherent and pulled away. She held on until she realized that he was only giving himself room to remove her T-shirt. She cooperated, but even that brief time out of his arms made her ache. How could she ever bear to let him go again? How could she continue to resist him when she wanted and needed him so badly?

There was nothing waiting for her outside this house that could compare with the way Case made her feel, she realized in sudden clarity.

Exotic locations? Case took her there whenever he touched her.

Mountain climbing? Nothing could ever take her higher than Case's lovemaking.

New and exhilarating experiences? She'd found them already with Case—and knew there was so much more to come.

Travel held no appeal if it took her away from Case. There could be no real adventure without him. Any happiness she might find would pale in comparison to the joy she found in his caresses. In the way he smiled at her and murmured her name.

Their clothes fell softly, silently, to the carpet. They moved together again, and this time the heat they generated was almost unbearable. Maddie cried out in pleasure and in need. Case patiently, inexorably, fed the flames, his hands stroking, squeezing, slipping between them to take her higher.

Her knees weakened. He held her up when she would have folded to the floor. He kissed her, roughly, possessively.

Needing to know he burned with her, Maddie returned the kisses with passionate abandon. She moved against him, caressing him with her body, her breasts brushing his chest, her smooth legs sliding slowly against his harder, rougher ones. This time, it was she who reached between them. Her hand was filled with pulsing, burning steel.

Case groaned. And then they were on the floor. She hadn't been able to support him when his knees had given way.

She laughed in delight that she'd been able to weaken him. He kissed the laughter from her lips, changing it to deep, ragged moans of pleasure. Moans he echoed when she arched to receive him.

Maddie was certain that the explosion that came then was more spectacular, more amazing, more incredibly dazzling than any fireworks display could ever have been. Her eyes filled with tears at the sheer beauty of it.

She glanced up at him, and was stunned to see that Case's beautiful gray eyes were moist, too. Could it possibly have been as perfect for him as it had been for her?

Could he know that at some point during the past few hours a decision had been made that would change both of their lives forever?

"Maddie." His voice was rough, his hands unsteady when he cupped her damp, flushed face between them. "Oh, God, Maddie, I need you. I want this house to be a home. *Our* home. When are you going to admit that you want that as badly as I do?"

"Now," she whispered, surrendering to the inevitable, praying she wouldn't regret her capitulation.

He went very still, his eyes searching her face, as though he was afraid he'd misunderstood. "Are you saying—"

"I'm saying that I'm keeping the promise I made to you on that beach in Cancún," she said, clutching her courage in both hands. "I'll marry you, Case. Whenever you want."

She hadn't expected the slight frown that creased his forehead. "You're marrying me only because you made me a promise? Only because you feel obligated to keep your word?"

It pleased her that he wanted more from her than that—even though he still hadn't said the words she so badly needed to hear from him. "No, Case," she said evenly. "I'm not marrying you because I feel obligated. I'm not marrying you for your money, or this house, or because my grandfather told me I had to," she added with a slight smile.

He moistened his lips. "Then why *are* you marrying me?"

"Because I love you," she said bravely. "And because I can't bear the thought of living without you ever again."

"Maddie." This time, she knew she wasn't mistaken about the tears in his eyes. He pressed his forehead to hers. "You won't regret it. I swear I won't ever give you cause to regret this. I pledge my life to you, Maddie Carmichael. Everything I have, everything I am—it's yours."

What about your love, Case? Do I have that, too?

But that was the one question she found herself incapable of asking. Perhaps because the answer was more important to her than life itself.

He kissed her with a tenderness that brought a lump to her throat. She returned the kiss with a joy tinged with a bittersweet sadness that she hoped she concealed from him.

12

ON THE FIRST Saturday morning in August, Case Brannigan began to whistle as he worked on the knot of his bow tie. Lying on the huge four-poster bed behind him—one of the few pieces of furniture he and Maddie had already purchased for the house—was the jacket to his black tux. A marriage license and plain gold band were tucked into the pockets of that jacket. He smiled at the thought of the diamond engagement ring that would accompany that band. He'd bought it the day after Maddie had finally agreed again to marry him, and she'd been wearing it since.

He hadn't seen Maddie in twenty-four hours, not since the rehearsal for the wedding. In fact, she'd been so busy during the month he'd given her to prepare that he'd hardly seen her at all the past few weeks. He could hardly wait for this to be over so that Maddie would finally be his. At last.

He glanced at his watch and winced. Damn, he was going to have to hurry or he'd be late for his own wedding. He'd gotten up early that morning to paint one of the upstairs bedrooms—the one they'd decided would make a nice nursery—and the time had slipped away from him.

Maddie would probably strangle him if he didn't show up promptly for this wedding. And he couldn't say he'd blame her.

Patting his pockets to make sure he had everything, Case hurried out of the house, locking the front door behind him. He and Maddie would be coming back here to pick up his bags before they headed for the airport to begin their honeymoon. He smiled at the thought of her surprise when she learned their destination. To her amused exasperation, he'd kept his plans a secret, promising her she would like the surprise he'd arranged for her.

His Grand Cherokee waited for him in front of the house, gleaming from a fresh wash-and-wax. Everything was going like clockwork, he thought with satisfaction. He was leaving ten minutes later than he'd planned, but he still had plenty of time to . . .

A loud, cracking noise from behind him caught his attention. He whirled, but saw no one. He reached for the door of his vehicle, then looked around again, sensing that something was wrong.

Everything looked normal. Nothing out of place. Except for one thing.

Frowning, he dropped his hand from the driver's door handle. His gaze was focused on the old-fashioned storm shelter that had been built into a grassy slope at the back of his yard. Other than to glance down into it and note that it had not been well-maintained, Case hadn't bothered with the shelter, having vague plans to dig it up and replace it with a swimming pool. The double doors of the concrete bunker had been closed and padlocked last time he'd checked. Now they stood wide open.

A whisper of warning sounded in Case's mind. Torn between hurrying to his wedding and securing his home, he hesitated for a moment, then sighed and started toward the shelter. He'd never be able to leave without knowing who'd been on his property. And why.

Maddie would forgive him for being a few minutes late if she knew he was guarding their home, he decided.

Though he approached carefully, he saw no one around the storm shelter. He paused at the open doors, his head cocked as he tried to identify the faint noise coming from inside it. It sounded like—static?

"Who's in there?" he demanded, wishing for a moment that he still carried a weapon.

There was no response to his challenge—only more of the faint, hissing static he'd heard before.

"Damn it," he muttered, knowing he couldn't leave without finding out what the hell was going on.

He took a step into the shelter.

Later, he would say his awareness of rapidly passing time and his anticipation of his wedding night had distracted him, making him temporarily forget all his years of training and experience. He hadn't been expecting an ambush, he would say defensively. Why should he have been?

The attack came just as he set his left foot on the first step down into the cellar. Though his leg had grown stronger during the past months, the force of the shove from behind him buckled it beneath him. Arms flailing for balance, he pitched forward.

He heard the mocking laughter just as his head hit something solid, hit so hard it snapped his neck back and sent an explosion of pain crashing through him.

The laughter and the pain merged, blended, swirled inside his skull. And then faded to black.

MADDIE STARED at the full-length mirror in the church dressing room and wondered if the reflection could possibly be her own. She hardly recognized herself in the delicate clouds of white lace and netting.

Her dress had been purchased off the rack—there hadn't been any other choice since Case had been so impatient to be married that he'd given her only a month to prepare. Still, the gown was beautiful. A fitted bodice with a deep, sweetheart neckline. A full, sweeping skirt and train. Long, sheer-lace sleeves, puffed at the shoulders. Zillions of tiny pearls worked into the lace. On her swept-up, freshly gold-streaked hair was a pearl and lace headpiece to which was attached a long, wispy veil. It was the kind of romantic, traditional wedding ensemble Maddie had always vaguely fantasized about wearing someday.

Case wanted this wedding to be picture-perfect, he'd told her. Bridesmaid, flower girl, wedding cake and champagne, all the trimmings they would have missed at that hasty ceremony in Cancún. He'd even chosen a best man. Many people, including Maddie, had found it quite amusing that the man he'd asked to stand up for him was Jackson Babbit.

"What time is it?" she asked, watching her rose-glossed lips move in the mirror.

Standing behind Maddie in a tea-length gown of midnight blue organdy, Jill checked her watch. "It's ten fifty-six," she said, then reached up to straighten the spray of flowers clipped to one side of her dark hair. "Four more minutes."

Four minutes. Maddie swallowed and pressed a hand to her stomach. Her Aunt Anita was directing the wedding, and would be sending Mike in any minute to summon Jill and Maddie to the church foyer.

Noticing Maddie's gesture, Jill laughed. "Nervous?"

"A little," Maddie admitted with a smile. "I keep thinking of all those people out there waiting to watch me walk down the aisle. It would have been easier if Case and I had just found another justice of the peace somewhere."

"Your dad would have been heartbroken. He says he's been looking forward to that walk down the aisle for years."

"I know," Maddie said with a misty smile. "He swears he'll feel Mother walking with us."

"Maybe he will."

A soft tap on the dressing-room door made both women look around.

"You suppose they've gotten started a few minutes early?" Jill asked.

Maddie gulped. "Wish me luck."

Jill smiled and brushed a careful kiss across Maddie's cold cheek. "You don't need luck. You have Case."

Maddie smiled and relaxed. "You're right. I do."

Jill opened the door while Maddie made one last check of her appearance. "Jackson?" she heard Jill say in surprise. "I thought you were Mike. You're supposed to be in the pastor's office with Case."

Turning, Maddie heard Jackson say something in a low murmur. Jill gasped.

"What is it?" Maddie asked.

Jill bit her lower lip. Jackson looked uncomfortable. "Case isn't here yet," he said. "It's time to start and no one's seen him. Your dad's outside watching for him."

Maddie shook her head in exasperation. "If he's gotten caught up in painting or wallpapering or something, today of all days, I'll strangle him."

"He wouldn't paint on his wedding day," Jill protested.

Maddie chuckled. "Yes, he would," she said. "He's obsessed with finishing that house. And he insists on doing everything himself—he says it's just not as meaningful to hire someone to do the work."

Tugging at his tightly knotted bow tie, Jackson asked, "What do you want us to do until he gets here? Everyone expects the wedding to start in a couple of minutes. Your aunt is getting frantic."

"Tell her to have the organist play a few more numbers," Maddie instructed. "The guests will just have to be patient. I'm sure Case will be here any minute."

FORTY-FIVE MINUTES LATER, there was still no sign of the groom.

Maddie hung up the phone in the dressing room and turned slowly to face the people watching her so closely. Her father. Jill. Jackson. The pastor. Aunt Anita and Lisa.

The dressing room was getting crowded, she thought inconsequentially. Aunt Nettie would have been there, too, if Mike hadn't convinced her to stay in the sanctuary with Grampa.

"Still no answer at Case's house?" Jill asked unnecessarily.

Maddie shook her head, the veil tickling her cheeks with the movement. "No answer."

"He must be on his way," Jackson said bracingly.

Jill gave him a chiding look. "She's been calling for the past half hour. It doesn't take that long to get from Case's house to the church."

"Maybe his car's broken down," Anita suggested for the third or fourth time.

"Maybe," Maddie agreed, as she had each time. But she didn't believe it. A simple mechanical breakdown wouldn't have kept Case away. There was a phone in his Jeep. He'd have called for a ride if he needed one.

"Maddie?" Lisa spoke in a quiet, careful voice, as though she wasn't sure she really wanted to bring up the subject. "You don't think he—er—"

Maddie looked around that roomful of people who were all aware that Case had left her at the altar once before, and she saw her cousin's unspoken question mirrored in their lovingly anxious eyes.

They were beginning to wonder if Case had stood her up again, she realized. Funny. The possibility hadn't even occurred to her. Had he?

"No," she said aloud, her voice clear, positive. "Something has happened or he would be here."

Case hadn't stood her up. She believed that without a moment's qualm. She trusted him completely.

Which could only mean . . .

"Oh, God," she whispered, going cold with dread. "Something's happened to him. Something's really wrong."

Jackson seemed to come to a sudden decision. "I'm going out to his house," he said.

"I'm coming with you," Maddie announced, moving toward the door.

"No. You stay here. I'll call you from there," Jackson suggested.

Maddie shook her head. A sudden sense of urgency was growing inside her. Case was in trouble, she thought. She didn't know what was wrong—but she knew something was. And she was suddenly desperate to get to him. "No. I'm going."

She turned to her father and his sister. "Daddy, Aunt Anita, I know it's getting crazy out there, but I have to ask you to handle it however you think best, okay?"

"You're sure you don't want me to go with you?" Mike fretted.

"I need you here," she answered gently, rising to kiss his cheek.

"All right." He turned and ushered everyone but Jill out of the room, already taking charge.

Maddie swept past Jackson, already headed for the nearest exit.

Jill hurried after her. "Maddie, wait! Don't you want to change first? Your dress—"

Maddie hesitated, glanced down at the layers of heavy fabrics and lace and thought of the dozens of tiny buttons closing the back of the gown. It had taken her ages to get into all this garb—and she was too impatient now to go through all those steps in reverse. "No. Jackson, please. Let's go now."

He nodded. "My car's right outside."

Maddie clutched her full skirts in both hands and hurried after him.

"I'm coming with you," Jill said, tossing her nosegay onto a table as she rushed along behind them, barely avoiding stepping on Maddie's train.

Maddie nodded absently. All her concentration now was on getting to Case.

Jackson had his car ready. He seemed a bit surprised to see Jill, still dressed in her wedding finery, but he didn't comment. Maddie got into the front passenger seat, bundling her gown and veil around her. She reached up impatiently to rip the headpiece from her hair, freeing her from the veil, at least, which she draped carelessly over the back of her seat. Jill slid into the back, and Jackson left the crowded church parking lot in a burst of impatient speed.

JACKSON HAD JUST turned onto the road leading to Case's house, when Maddie caught a glimpse of movement in the woods that lined the country road. She turned her head in time to see two ATVs speeding through the trees, away from the road.

"Danny," she said, and spun to face Jackson. "I'm sure I just saw Danny Cooper and Steve Langford on their four-wheelers."

"I saw them," Jackson said grimly, and pressed harder on the accelerator. The car leapt forward.

"You don't think they've hurt Case, do you?" Jill asked from the back. "I mean, Danny's a little creep, but—"

"He hates Case," Maddie said, remembering the look on the boy's face at the festival. "I wouldn't put anything past him."

Jackson squealed to a stop in the driveway, behind Case's Grand Cherokee.

"His car's here. He has to be here, too," Maddie said, throwing her door open and leaping out of the car. "Case? Case!" She ran toward the house, stumbling over her skirts and petticoats but managing to keep her balance.

The front door was locked. She pounded on it, rang the bell. The house remained ominously silent.

Jackson rejoined her. "I've checked all the other doors," he said. "They're all locked."

"Oh, God. Where is he?"

"I'm going to break in and search the house. You and Jill go around back and check the garage and the yard."

Maddie was already running down the covered porch that wrapped around the side of the house. Jill followed closely behind her.

The garage doors were closed, but there was an access panel set into one outside wall. Maddie punched in the security code Case had taught her. The doors opened. The three-car garage was empty.

Hands pressed to her temples, she turned and scanned the yard. It was neatly mowed, the flower beds cleared of weeds and waiting to be replanted. Case had been working so hard, she thought with a catch in her breath.

Where was he?

"He's not inside," Jackson said, rushing up to join them. "I've looked everywhere."

"I think we should call the police," Jill said in a small voice.

Biting her lip, Maddie started to agree. She turned toward the kitchen door, which Jackson had opened from inside after entering the house through a window he'd broken. Something made her turn back and study the yard again.

Everything was still, quiet. The August sun burned directly overhead, hot and almost painfully bright. Something glittered in the sunlight, drawing Maddie's attention. The reflection came from a metal padlock on the double doors of the storm shelter at the back of the property.

Drawn by a compulsion she couldn't have explained, Maddie took a step in that direction, and then another. And then she was running again. "Case? *Case?*"

"Maddie, what is it?" Jackson was following behind her. Hampered by her high heels on the soft grass, Jill struggled to keep up.

Maddie stopped in front of the shelter. She pointed to the scuffed dirt around it, evidence that the doors had recently been opened, and what might have been ATV tracks leading away from the shelter and into the woods.

Studying those signs for only a moment, Jackson reached the same conclusion Maddie had. He leapt toward the wooden doors and pounded on them. "Case? Hey, Case, you in there?"

All of them waited with bated breath for an answer. There was nothing.

"Maybe he's not in there," Jill said. "He wouldn't have let the boys lock him in."

"Not if he was expecting them," Maddie agreed. "But what if they caught him by surprise?"

She knelt by the doors, her ear close to the weathered wood. She rested a hand against the door, and fancied that a ripple of electricity coursed through her with the contact. "He's in there," she whispered, looking up at Jackson. "I just know he is."

Jackson frowned, but rapped on the door again. "Case?" he shouted. "Can you hear us?"

"I think I hear something," Maddie whispered, trying to identify the faint, muffled sound. Could it have been a groan?

Suddenly frantic, she tugged futilely at the heavy lock. "We have to get this off. I have to see!" she cried, her throat tight.

Jackson put his hands on her shoulders and pulled her away. "You can't break it off with your hands. We need a crowbar."

Maddie strained against him, resisting his efforts to restrain her, her fear clouding her thoughts for the moment. Jackson shook her gently. "Maddie!" he said sharply, his voice penetrating the panic. "Does Case have a crowbar? Anything I can use to break this lock?"

She drew a deep breath and tried to think. "Look in the storage room in the garage," she murmured. "That's where he keeps his tools."

Jackson was already running back to the house.

Jill put an arm around Maddie's shoulders, but she didn't speak. She probably didn't know what to say.

Both of them were afraid that, if Case was inside that shelter, there was a reason he wasn't answering them.

It took Jackson fifteen minutes of straining and cursing to break the padlock. He threw open the doors. Afraid Case wouldn't be there—and almost as desperately afraid that he would be—Maddie stepped forward. The sunlight beamed down into the dank, shadowy cellar, providing just enough illumination for them to see the dark, crumpled shape lying at the foot of the concrete steps.

"Case!" Maddie screamed, and started to rush forward. Her foot caught in her petticoat. Jackson caught her just in time to keep her from tumbling right on top of Case's prone body. Together, they entered more carefully.

Ignoring dirt and cobwebs and unpleasant scurrying noises, Maddie knelt beside Case, reaching out a shaking hand to touch his pale cheek. There was blood on his face and in his hair, and his left leg was twisted at an uncomfortable angle. But he was breathing, she realized with a sob.

He was breathing.

"Case?" she whispered, her mouth close to his ear. "Case, can you hear me?"

He groaned and his eyelids fluttered.

"Case. It's me. Maddie. Open your eyes, darling."

He opened his eyes, though they were clouded and unfocused. "Maddie?" His voice was thick. "Did you call me darling?"

She caught her breath on a sob that might have been a broken laugh. "Yes," she whispered. "Oh, Case, are you all right?"

"Head hurts." He lifted his head cautiously and looked around. She could almost see his memory return as he began to curse beneath his breath.

Having seen that Case was all right, Jackson crossed the cramped, dirty room, his head bent to avoid contact with the low ceiling. He bent to pick up a cheap plastic, battery-operated radio that had been sitting in one corner, static pouring from its single speaker. "What the hell is this?" he asked as he turned off the grating sound.

Case pushed himself upright, with help from Maddie and Jill, who'd knelt at his other side. "That," he said grimly, "is what lured me down here. I was leaving for the church when I noticed the shelter doors were open. When I came over to close them, I heard the noise. I was just coming in to investigate when I was shoved from behind. I hit my head on that beam when I fell forward. Damn it."

Hearing the self-disgust in Case's voice, Maddie touched his grubby cheek, worrying that he might have a concussion. "Have you been unconscious ever since?"

"In and out, I think. I kept hearing the static, but I couldn't seem to wake up enough to do anything about it. I'm okay now, though," he added as though to reassure her.

She wasn't reassured. She fully intended to get him to a doctor as soon as possible.

"We think it was Danny and a friend who attacked you," Jill said, heated indignation coloring her voice. "We saw their ATVs in the woods."

Case's face hardened. "I'll cream the little—"

"You will let the authorities handle this," Maddie interrupted firmly. "Is that clear?"

He sighed. "Yeah," he muttered. "But they'd damned well better do something about those kids this time, or I'll handle it myself."

"Something will be done this time," Jackson said flatly. "I'll help you see to it."

"I'll go call an ambulance," Jill said, moving toward the steps.

Case shook his head, then pressed a hand to his temple as though the movement had made him dizzy. "No ambulance," he said. "What time is it?"

"Almost twelve-thirty," Jackson answered with a glance at his watch. "C'mon, Brannigan, let's get you out of here and over to the doctor's office."

"No," Case said, though he allowed Jackson to help him to his feet. "I have other plans." He glanced at Maddie's disheveled clothing. "Look at you," he scolded. "You're getting your skirts filthy. How's that going to look in the wedding photos, hmm?"

She caught her breath on a sob, then released it shakily. "I looked fabulous an hour ago," she answered in mock exasperation, relief making her a bit giddy. "I seem to have been stood up—again."

Case gave her a smile that melted her heart. "Oh, no, sweetheart. The wedding was just postponed—again."

Though he wasn't quite steady on his feet, he nodded toward the steps. "Come on. We have to catch the preacher before he decides to go fishing or something this afternoon."

Maddie blinked. "You want to go on with the wedding? Now?"

He brushed a kiss across her cheek. "I love you, Maddie. I don't want to wait any longer to make you my wife."

She stared at him, oblivious to their audience. "You've never said that before," she whispered.

He blinked, looking surprised. "I haven't?"

"No."

"Surely you knew."

"I wasn't sure," she admitted. "Not until an hour ago."

He seemed confused. "When I didn't show up for the wedding? How did that convince you?"

She smiled tremulously. "I knew with all my heart that you would have been there unless something had gone terribly wrong. You wouldn't have purposefully stood me up."

"Because I love you," he murmured. "More than life itself."

The realization had finally come to her in that church dressing room. Case wanted to marry her, not because she was convenient or compliant or any other reason that had worried her earlier. There were many other women he could have married if all he'd wanted was a wife—younger, prettier women, for that matter. But it had been Maddie he'd proposed to on that beach in Cancún. Maddie he'd thought of as he'd lain in that foreign hospital bed. Maddie he'd followed to Mitchell's Fork, Mississippi. And Maddie for whom he'd created a home, and with whom he wanted to start a family.

It was Maddie he wanted. Only her. Because he loved her.

Blinking back tears, she made one last attempt at being practical. "But what about calling the police? What about Danny and Steve?"

"Someone can call from the church. I'll make a statement as soon as I've said 'I do.' Now, are you coming or not?" He held out his hand, his eyes locked with hers, and in their silvery gray depths she saw the deep, heartfelt emotions that were difficult for this strong, complex man to express.

She placed her own hand in his slightly clammy palm. "Let's go."

MOST OF THE GUESTS were still at the church, curiosity having kept them there talking and speculating. Clearly fascinated by the turn of events, they hurried back to their seats when a flustered Anita tried to regain control of the ceremony.

The organist had left, having other plans for the afternoon. One of the guests knew how to play, and was hastily pressed into service. The flower girl had fallen asleep in her mother's lap, and had to be awakened, yawning and heavy-eyed, but sweetly cooperative.

The groom's and best man's tuxedos were wrinkled and dusty, and there was a jagged rip in one leg of the groom's pants. He was limping badly on his reinjured left leg, though he stood straight and tall as he waited for his bride. His hair was still a bit disheveled and matted in one spot with dried blood. His face was pale and bruised. He'd washed hastily, and had missed a smudge of blood at his temple. Doc Adcock sat ready to examine him the moment the ceremony ended. But the groom was smiling.

The bridesmaid's midnight blue dress was dusty at the hem and her dainty, dyed-to-match shoes were grubby. Her flowers were starting to wilt, as were the ones in the bride's bouquet.

The bride was beautiful. No one seemed to notice that her veil was wrinkled, that tendrils of hair had escaped her careful upsweep, or that the hem of her lacy gown was dirty and ripped in a couple of places. Nor, of course, could anyone know that there was a long, jagged run in one stocking, hidden by her long, full skirts.

Many of the guests would say later that it was the most touching, most lovingly sincere exchange of vows they'd ever witnessed.

Maddie would always agree.

Epilogue

"WHERE IS CASE? What could possibly be keeping him?"

Maddie Brannigan managed a shaky smile at the near panic in her father's voice. "Don't worry, Dad. Case will be here in time."

Standing beside the hospital bed on which she lay, Mike tried to look reassured. "I hope you're right, honey. I'm just not prepared to step in as a labor coach. Back in my day, men stayed out in the waiting room during this sort of thing."

"Times have changed, Daddy," she murmured, then caught her breath as another contraction ripped through her.

Mike groaned in sympathy, patted his daughter's hand and again wished aloud for his son-in-law to arrive.

To everyone's relief, Case rushed in only minutes later. "Am I too late?" he demanded, hastily tying a paper scrub suit over the uniform he wore beneath it.

"No," Maddie assured him, tears of relief in her eyes. "You're just in time."

Mike eagerly relinquished his place at her side to her husband. "Let me know when it's over," he called over his shoulder as he bolted from the labor room.

Zachary Michael Brannigan was born an hour later, nine and a half months after his parent's wedding day. He had been conceived during a long, adventurous honeymoon in Europe, the groom's gift to his bride. Despite a concussion and a sprained ankle, the groom had made that honeymoon a memory for the bride to treasure for a lifetime.

After the scandal that had sent Danny Cooper and his friend Steve Langford to military school—the boys had sworn they hadn't intended to hurt Case, that they'd only been playing a practical joke by locking him in the storm cellar on his wedding day—Case had been persuaded by a group of Mitchell's Fork citizens to run as an independent candidate for sheriff in the next election. He'd won easily, though he'd ruefully said on more than one occasion that he couldn't imagine why he'd allowed himself to be convinced. He hadn't really intended to remain in law enforcement, but Maddie suspected he enjoyed the job more than he would admit.

Surprisingly enough, Case had been supported by Major Cooper, who'd received a rude awakening when he'd realized that his overindulged son could have killed Case with his cruel and vindictive actions. Cooper claimed that he hadn't truly realized until then that his son had gotten so far out of control.

It had been Case who'd recommended military school, followed by a stint in the service. He'd explained that Danny would benefit more from the discipline and training he would receive in the military than from the adverse influence he'd be exposed to if he was sent to jail for assault and battery or any of the other charges Case could have brought against him. Cooper had gratefully agreed.

Propped against the pillows in her hospital room, Maddie rested from the delivery and watched her husband rock his tiny son, a look of adoring wonder on Case's lean, strong face. She tried to speak past a lump in her throat. "Well, Sheriff? What do you have to say for yourself this time? You almost stood up me *and* your son."

Case gave her a sheepish smile. "There was a chemical spill out on the highway. No one was hurt, but someone had to supervise the cleanup."

"That someone being you."

He nodded. "But I came as soon as Jackson tracked me down to tell me that you'd gone into labor during the wedding shower for him and Jill. He was frantic to get me here in time, and I'm grateful to him. I wouldn't have missed this for anything short of disaster, Maddie."

She smiled. "I know, darling. I knew you would be here."

He didn't return the smile. Instead, he looked from her to their sleeping son. When his eyes lifted again, they glittered with emotion. "I love you, Maddie."

It was still something he said rarely, only on very special occasions. Like this one. The words were all the more special to Maddie because she knew how sincerely he meant them.

Case Brannigan had a home and a family now. And he would never take them for granted.

He'd been looking for them all his life.

This month's
irresistible novels from

Temptation

JESSIE'S LAWMAN by Kristine Rolofson

Trapped by a snowstorm, Jessica Carter spent one passion-filled evening with Sheriff Daniel MacAdams. Four years later, she returned curious about the sexy lawman, the child she'd left behind and the magical memories of that one night together...

FOR RICHER OR POORER by JoAnn Ross

Bachelor Arms

Bachelor Arms was a new beginning for Lily Van Cortlandt and her unborn baby. She would never again trust a lying, cheating rich boy. Mac Sullivan was the kind of man she wanted. Hardworking. Honest. Ordinary. *Except Mac was lying about who he was...*

NAUGHTY BY NIGHT by Tiffany White

Secret Fantasies

People had expected Ashleigh Frost to be good all her life, but now she'd decided to be bad. She was going to make men sweat. She was going to make Detective Cade Hawkins sweat. She was going to fulfil his every fantasy!

I WON'T! by Gina Wilkins

Grooms on the Run

Swept off her feet by sexy Case Brannigan when on holiday, Maddie Carmichael couldn't believe he'd left her waiting at the altar and then arrogantly presumed she would just go home and wait for him...

Spoil yourself next month
with these four novels from

Temptation

STRANGER IN MY ARMS by Madeline Harper

Secret Fantasies

Do you have a secret fantasy? Kasey Halliday does. She's always wanted to be swept off her feet by a dark, handsome stranger. Will Eastman, Kasey's enigmatic new neighbour, fits the bill perfectly. But when mysterious accidents start to occur, Kasey realizes more than just her heart is in danger...

THE TEXAN by Janice Kaiser

The 500th Temptation

Brady Coleman vowed to bring his sister's killer to justice. But the rough-and-tumble Texan desperately needed the help of beautiful Jane Stewart. And when her vulnerable heart longed for Brady, how could she refuse?

JILT TRIP by Heather MacAllister

Grooms on the Run

Carter Belden was *not* having a good day. He was supposed to be getting married, but his best man was late, his pager wouldn't stop bleeping and then he was kidnapped before the ceremony—by his ex-wife!

THREE GROOMS AND A WEDDING by JoAnn Ross

Bachelor Arms

Ever since Blythe Fielding had hired private investigator Gage Remington to solve a decades-old mystery, she had had second thoughts about walking down the aisle with her fiancé. Gage was sexy, dangerous and compelling. How could Blythe resist the unknown passion his eyes promised her?

Temptation

THREE GROOMS:

Case, Carter and Mike

TWO WORDS:

"We Don't!"

ONE MINI-SERIES:

GROOMS ON THE RUN

Starting in March 1996, Mills & Boon Temptation brings you this exciting new mini-series.

Each book (and there'll be one a month for three months) features a sexy hero who's ready to say "I do!" but ends up saying, "I don't!"

Look out for these special Temptations:

In March, I WON'T! by Gina Wilkins
In April, JILT TRIP by Heather MacAllister
In May, NOT THIS GUY! by Glenda Sanders

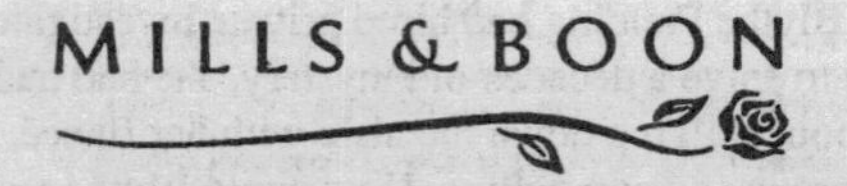